ROZ PARK

C000183084

THE POCKET GUIDE TO
SALTWATER FISHES
OF
BRITAIN AND EUROPE

THE POCKET GUIDE TO
SALTWATER FISHES
OF
BRITAIN AND EUROPE

Alwyne Wheeler

Illustrated by Colin Newman

**DRAGON'S
WORLD**

Dragon's World Ltd
Limpsfield
Surrey RH8 0DY
Great Britain

First published by Dragon's World 1992

Editor: Patricia Burgess
Designer: Carole Perks
Art Director: Dave Allen
Editorial Director: Pippa Rubinstein

*The author would like to acknowledge the contribution made to this
book by Mrs Sita Fonseka, who undertook the typing of the
manuscript, and spared no effort to meet the deadline.*

The catalogue record for this book is available from
the British Library

ISBN 1 80528 158 0

Typeset by Dragon's World Ltd, London

Printed in Singapore

Contents

Introduction

The geographical position of the British Isles results in their having a relatively rich fish fauna in terms of species as well as potentially abundant fisheries. The latter is due to some extent to this group of islands being on the edge of a continent, thus having a wide continental shelf (a shallow, gently shelving region between the land and the deep sea) which offers an extensive area of sheltered shallow water which sunlight penetrates to stimulate the growth of plants and animals. The abundance of fish is also due to the influence of the North Atlantic Drift, a major current sweeping north-eastwards across the Atlantic from tropical waters, causing sea temperatures and climate to be considerably warmer than geographical latitude might otherwise suggest.

The marine fish fauna is composed of several elements, which together amount to a surprisingly large number of species (about 250 in total). One of the most important groups includes fishes which are most abundant in the cold northern Atlantic. These include valuable commercial species such as herring, cod, haddock, saithe and halibut, some of which are true Arctic species with close relatives in the North Pacific. Others are small species such as the sea scorpions, the hooknose, viviparous blenny and lumpsucker, many of which occur commonly in the north of Europe and some also on the North American coast.

Many British sea fishes, however, are also found to the south, many of them in the Mediterranean, and it is this element of the fauna that adds so much interest. This group includes the blennies, gobies, wrasses, pipefishes, seabass, grey mullets and most of the flatfishes. Many of these fish or their closest relatives occur in the Mediterranean. These waters are much warmer than the seas around the British Isles, so it is not surprising that those species which live there and occur as far north as Britain are often migratory, moving northwards in summer. Some examples of such migratory fishes include the tunny (which may actually migrate from the Mediterranean), stingray, sea breams and the pilchard.

A third source of fishes for the British fauna is the tropical Atlantic, and some of the most exciting and perhaps rarest fishes originate in this area. Some of them are probably accidental wanders, such as the sailfish found in South Devon in 1928, and the white marlin in Morecambe Bay more recently. Other large species from the warmer Atlantic which have also been reported once only include the yellow fin tunny, the big-eyed tunny and the tarpon, while some, such as the smooth pufferfish, have been found several times. An interesting development of the 1980s and 1990s has been the increased occurrence of such species as the trigger-fish. Up to the 1970s it was considered to be a rare fish which occurred two or three times a year, mainly on the south coast, but it became much more abundant in the 1980s and is now caught quite commonly. In this case it is not certain whether this fish has colonized British coasts from the tropical Atlantic or from the Lusitanian fauna of Portugal and Spain, for it occurs in both regions.

To the south of the British Isles fish species are increasingly of southern origin, most also occurring in the Mediterranean, but others being most abundant off the western coast of Africa. The fish fauna of the Atlantic coast is therefore composed of the same elements as those of the British Isles, with the cold northern Atlantic species decreasing to the south and being replaced sometimes by related southern species, and at others by forms which occupy the same ecological niche.

The fish fauna of the Mediterranean is more homogeneous, although the distribution of fish within it is uneven. Generally speaking, the same fishes are found along the northern coasts of the Mediterranean. The southern coastline is poorer in species and originally the fauna of the south-eastern basin was poorest of all, although it was very specialized and many species were extremely abundant. The Adriatic, however, has a number of species which are found nowhere else in the Mediterranean basin (or elsewhere for that matter). The reasons for these distributions can be attributed to the geological history and latitude of the Mediterranean. The northern coasts are often rocky, interspersed with sand, and offer varied habitats; the southern coasts are mainly sandy and the habitats less varied (they are also much hotter), while in the south-eastern corner of the Mediterranean the enormous influence of the fresh water and silt from the River Nile could be detected for hundreds of miles from its mouth.

The control of the Nile's flow by the Aswan and other dams has made a considerable difference to the hydrography of the area and has also affected fisheries. However, other man-induced changes have produced alterations in the fauna. A substantial part of the fauna of the south-eastern Mediterranean is composed of immigrants from the Red Sea via the Suez Canal. Some of these so-called Lessepian migrants are now so abundant on the coast of Israel and Egypt that they are commercially fished; others have spread as far as southern Greece and westwards as far as Tunisia.

All round the coasts of Europe enormous changes have taken place in the abundance of fishes. Mostly these have been due to virtually uncontrolled fishing by fishermen who have developed techniques to maximize catches of the target species, or switched from one species to another as populations varied. Thus, over the years crises have developed in herring, pilchard, mackerel, cod and sole fisheries, while species such as tuna and swordfish have become rare or uncommon, even in the Mediterranean where they were once abundant. In contrast to these often well-publicized events, the virtual disappearance of large sharks and rays in most European seas (particularly in the Mediterranean) has gone unnoticed. Few sharks are caught deliberately, but many are killed in capturing tunny or other fishes; bottom trawls also catch rays almost from the newly hatched stage. Both sharks and rays, which produce relatively few young and are a long time in attaining maturity are particularly vulnerable to exploitation, even if it is accidental.

The sea fishes of Europe have to be seen as a dynamic system, changing with oceanic conditions, possibly also with climatic conditions, and very much affected by human activities. These all contribute to making their study particularly interesting.

ALWYNE WHEELER

Lamprey

Petromyzon marinus

Family name Petromyzontidae (lampreys)
Length 70-90cm (28–36in), exceptionally to 120cm (47½ in)
Weight approx. 2.5kg (5lb 8oz)

Identification Eel-like in shape but with a sucker disc. Teeth on sucker disc small at edges, larger and pointed towards centre; tooth plate near oral opening with 7–9 large, sharp cusps. Eyes small; seven separate gill openings on each side of head. No true rayed fins but a fold of skin like a fin on back and tail. Coloration: olive to yellow brown, heavily blotched with black and dark brown.

Habitat In marine life-stage is found attached to large fishes and to the basking shark. Lamprey scars have been commonly seen on small whales and dolphins. It is unlikely that they feed on the shark or the cetaceans, but are probably hitching a lift. Rarely caught free-swimming in the sea.

Food Sucks blood and body fluids from fishes.

Breeding Breeds in fresh water from spring to midsummer.

Range Found off the coasts of northern Europe and eastern North America, and often far out to sea. Now rare in many regions due to estuarine development (dams, weirs) and pollution. A threatened species in Europe.

Porbeagle
Lamna nasus

Family name Lamnidae (mackerel sharks)
Length 3m (10ft)
Weight maximum 226.5kg (500lb), more commonly
90.8kg (200lb)

Identification A large round-bodied, thickset shark which
has a tubby appearance. Five moderately large gill slits. First
dorsal fin origin above the pectoral fin bases; the second dorsal
fin, very small in comparison, is directly above the similar-
sized anal fin. Tail fin large, upper lobe high. A strong keel on
the sides of the tail with a smaller keel beneath it. Teeth large
and triangular with a small cusp each side of the base of the
tooth. Coloration: deep blue to greyish-blue above, merging
gradually into cream colour on the underside.
Habitat Lives in the surface and near-surface layers of the
ocean, rarely penetrating inshore waters on exposed coasts.
Food Eats mostly schooling, open-ocean fishes (mackerel,
herring, garfish, etc.) and large numbers of squids.
Breeding Live-bearing, producing 1–5 young at a time.
Young 50–60cm (19½–24in) at birth. Probably breeds every
2–3 years.
Range Widely distributed in the North Atlantic (from
Norway and Iceland south to Morocco) and in the
Mediterranean.

Basking Shark
Cetorhinus maximus

Family name Cetorhinidae (basking shark)
Length 11m (35ft), possibly larger; average about
7.6m (25ft)
Weight estimated at 3000kg (3 tons)

Identification In European seas size alone will identify a
basking shark, and confusion is only likely with medium-sized
whales, which have horizontal tail flukes. The basking shark
has five massive gill slits, which virtually circle the posterior
head. Jaw teeth are minute, close-set and flattened, and the gill
arches have long thin rakers on their inner sides. Young sharks
have a peculiar bottle-nosed appearance. Coloration: greyish-
brown, nearly black on the back and sides, with a paler grey-
blotched underside.
Habitat Mainly off the oceanic coasts of northern Europe
and in the high seas. Is occasionally seen cruising in the
surface waters, but may hibernate near the ocean bed.
Food A plankton feeder; it swims through the plankton-rich
surface waters with its mouth wide open. Much of its food is
minute crustaceans, but large quantities of fish larvae and
other animals are swallowed incidentally.
Breeding Believed to give birth to one pup at a time and
possibly every five years. The young are around 1.5m (5ft)
long at birth.
Range Widely distributed across the North Atlantic; rare in
the Mediterranean.

Thresher Shark
Alopias vulpinus

Family name Alopiidae (thresher sharks)
Length maximum 6m (20ft); usually 3–4m (10–13ft)
Weight maximum approx. 127kg (280lb)

Identification The enormously long tail fin, with the upper lobe as long as the body, is characteristic. The snout is short and rounded. Five rather small gill slits, the last two above the front edge of the pectoral fins. Mouth moderate in size; teeth in jaws small and triangular. First dorsal fin high, its base entirely in front of the pelvic fins; second dorsal fin small, also in front of the equally small anal fin. Coloration: grey-blue to dark grey on the back, white ventrally, except for light grey under the snout.
Habitat Lives in the surface waters of the ocean, mostly far offshore, but entering coastal waters from time to time, mostly in summer. Probably a summer migration into British seas from the open ocean.
Food Eats schooling fishes (mackerel, herring, garfish) which are said to be herded into panicking schools by the long tail; also eats squids.
Breeding Live-bearing, producing 2–4 pups at a time, each about 1.5m (5ft) at birth.
Range From northern Norway to Morocco and the Mediterranean; also found off the east coast of North America.

Dogfish

Scyliorhinus canicula

Family name Scyliorhinidae (dogfishes or catsharks)
Length up to 1m (39in); usually around 60cm (24in)
Weight maximum 1.72kg (3lb 12oz)

Identification A small shark, which has a long but low tail
following the outline of the body; the lower lobe of the tail fin
is scarcely developed. Dorsal fins small, the first dorsal
completely behind the pelvic fin base. The nostrils are widely
spaced, each covered with a broad flap; the two flaps are
almost joined in the mid-line. Coloration: warm sandy brown
with small, dark brown spots on back and sides; underside
cream-coloured.
Habitat A small, bottom-living shark found in shallow,
inshore water of 3–10m (2–60 fathoms). The young fish are
most common in shallow water. The adult lives on sand or
fine gravel bottoms and occasionally over mud.
Food Eats a wide range of bottom-living invertebrates, but
mainly shrimps and crabs, worms and whelks.
Breeding The eggs are laid in oblong brown cases with long
tendrils at each corner, which fasten the egg to wrecks,
seaweed or other hard structures. Egg-laying is mainly in
shallow water throughout winter and spring.
Range Widespread from southern Norway to the Canary
Islands and throughout the Mediterranean; all round the
British Isles.

Nursehound
Scyliorhinus stellaris

Family name Scyliorhinidae (dogfishes or catsharks)
Length maximum 1.5m (5ft); usually about 1.2m (4ft)
Weight maximum 9.5kg (21lb)

Identification A very similar species to the dogfish, with a
low tail fin running in line with the body; lower lobe of the tail
fin poorly developed. The dorsal fins are small and rounded
with the origin of the first dorsal fin just above the end of the
pelvic fin base. Nostrils widely spaced, each covered with a
broad flap. The two flaps are separated by a wide space.
Coloration: sandy to dark brown back with large, darker
brown blotches forming saddles across it. The underside is
creamy white.
Habitat A bottom-living shark of inshore waters in depths of
1–2m (3–6ft 6in) down to 63m (35 fathoms). It lives on
rough, rocky bottoms and seems to be more solitary than the
common dogfish.
Food A wide range of crustaceans, molluscs (including
octopuses) and bottom-living fishes.
Breeding Lays its eggs mainly in spring and summer among
algae and on wrecks. Eggs are laid in oblong, brown, leathery
cases with long tendrils at the corners; these tendrils twine
among the seaweed.
Range From southern Norway to the Canary Islands and
throughout the Mediterranean. All round the British Isles, but
least common in the North Sea.

Tope

Galeorhinus galeus

Family name Carcharinidae (requiem sharks)
Length maximum about 1.67m (5½ ft); usually about
1.2m (4 ft)
Weight maximum 33.9kg (74lb)

Identification A slender-bodied shark with a moderate-sized
first dorsal fin, a slightly smaller second dorsal fin and a well-
developed tail fin with a large lower lobe. The snout is rather
prominent and rounded, and there is a small spiracle behind
the eye. Jaw teeth are triangular, sharply pointed; in the sides
of the jaws they are oblique, with serrations on the shorter
edge; in the centre of the jaws they are upright and serrated
both sides. Coloration: uniform grey or greyish-brown on the
back and upper sides, white ventrally.
Habitat An inshore shark found in shallow water, the smaller
specimens in 3–10m (1.6–5.5 fathoms) and the larger ones
down to 200m (109 fathoms). Although it may live close to
the bottom, it is usually found mid-water in small schools.
Food Mostly schooling fishes such as whiting, pouting and
cod; it also eats squids and some bottom-living organisms.
Breeding Live-bearing, giving birth to 20–40 young at a
time, usually in late summer in shallow water. The young are
about 40cm (15¾in) at birth.
Range From northern Norway and Iceland to Morocco and
throughout the Mediterranean.

Blue Shark

Prionace glauca

Family name Carcharinidae (requiem sharks)
Length maximum about 3.83m (12ft 7in); in European seas 2.7m (9ft)
Weight maximum 151kg (333lb), but rarely more than 45.5kg (100lb)

Identification A long, slender-bodied, streamlined shark, with a long and high upper lobe to its tail. The pectoral fins are very long and smoothly curved. The snout is extremely long and smoothly pointed. No spiracle behind the eye. The teeth are sharply pointed, slightly oblique and have serrated edges. Coloration: back and upper sides a beautiful deep indigo blue, the sides lighter; underside clear white. The blue soon fades to grey after death.
Habitat A surface-living shark of the open sea, which is only rarely seen in inshore waters, and then on open ocean coasts. The nearest it comes inshore is about 24km (15 miles)
Food Eats surface-living fishes, mackerel, herring, pilchard, garfish and squids in large numbers. Often follows fishing boats to pick up discarded fish and offal.
Breeding Live-bearing, giving birth to litters or 20–60 young, mostly in summer. The number depends on the size of the mother; they are about 38cm (15in) at birth.
Range From southern Norway and off the oceanic western coasts of the British Isles, southwards to southern Africa and throughout the Mediterranean. Cosmopolitan in warm temperate and tropical seas.

Hammerhead

Sphyrna zygaena

Family name Sphyrnidae (hammerhead sharks)
Length up to 4m (13ft)

Identification In European seas this shark is unmistakable because of its head shape, with the sides of the head forming conspicuous lobes, at the end of which the nostrils and eyes are sited. The whole front of the head is flattened from top to bottom. The shape of the 'hammer' in front is smoothly rounded, with an indentation in front of each nostril. The first dorsal fin is large, the second much smaller; the tail fin is developed, the upper lobe very long. Coloration: the back olive-brown or greyish above; light grey ventrally.

Habitat A mid-water shark which is also frequently seen close to the sea bed. Rare in all European seas, exceptionally so in British waters.

Food Eats bottom-living invertebrates, shrimps, crabs and squids, and a wide range of fishes. Potentially dangerous to humans.

Breeding Live-bearing; up to 37 young in a litter.

Range Strongly migratory, moving into cooler seas in summer; huge schools of this and other hammerheads have been reported migrating off the African coast. Rarely found off Europe, but worldwide in warm temperate seas.

Starry Smoothhound
Mustelus asterias

Family name Triakidae (smoothhounds)
Length maximum 1.8m (6ft); usually around 1.2m (4ft)
Weight maximum 12.70kg (28lb)

Identification Slender-bodied shark with a rounded snout
and two dorsal fins which are moderately large; the second is
only slightly smaller than the first. Tail fin large with well-
developed upper and lower lobes. Five gill slits and a large
spiracle just behind the eye. Teeth blunt, forming a flat,
pavement-like surface. Coloration: grey on the back and upper
sides, with numerous creamy-white spots; creamy white on the
underside.
Habitat An inshore shark, which usually lives close to the sea
bed at depths of 70m (38 fathoms). It is most common on
sandy and gravel bottoms.
Food Eats crustaceans almost solely. Its diet includes hermit
crabs, edible and shore crabs and squat lobsters.
Breeding Live-bearing, producing litters of 7–15, depending
on the size of the mother; the young are about 30cm (12in) in
length.
Range The most common smoothhound in northern
European seas, ranging from Denmark to Morocco and
throughout the Mediterranean. Two similar species occur in
the Mediterranean, but these lack the white spots.

Spurdog
Squalus acanthias

Family name Squalidae (spurdogs; spiny hounds)
Length maximum 1.2m (4ft); rarely more than 1m (39in)
Weight maximum 9.5kg (21lb)

Identification A slender-bodied shark which has a sharp spine in the front of each dorsal fin, the second one being larger, even though the fin is smaller. The tail is relatively large and broad. The anal fin is absent. The snout is pointed; there is a spiracle behind each eye; five gill slits just in front of each pectoral fin. Teeth in both jaws oblique, with sharp cusps. Coloration: dark grey or grey-brown above, lighter ventrally with scattered white spots on the back and sides.

Habitat Lives in large, often single-sex schools just above the sea bed in depths of 10–200m (5–110 fathoms). Often caught near the surface, especially at night.

Food Schooling fishes, particularly herring, sprat, sandeels, whiting and garfish. It also eats a large amount of bottom-living invertebrates.

Breeding Live-bearing, producing litters of 3–11 young, each of which is around 30cm (12in) long. Gestation lasts between 18 and 22 months.

Range North Atlantic from northern Norway to Morocco, Iceland, southern Greenland and down the eastern coast of North America. Also in the Mediterranean and Black Sea.

Monkfish
Squatina squatina

Family name Squatinidae (angel sharks)
Length maximum 1.8m (6ft); females are larger than males
Weight maximum 29.94kg (66lb)

Identification Immediately identifiable in northern
European seas as it is the only shark with enormously
expanded pectoral and pelvic fins, giving a very wide body,
flattened from above. The head is broad, with a broad mouth
placed at the end of it; very wide flared nostrils above the
edges of the mouth opening, each covered with a broad, fringe
flap. Spiracles very large, well spaced behind the eyes.
Coloration: sandy-brown or greyish, densely dotted with
darker markings; white ventrally.
Habitat A bottom-living shark which is most common on
sand or mud in depths of 9–91m (3–50 fathoms). It lies
partially buried on the sea bed. However, it is a powerful
swimmer in mid-water.
Food Almost entirely bottom-living fishes, particularly
flatfish, such as dab, sole, plaice and small rays and dogfish.
Breeding Live-bearing; litters of 9–20. The young, about
24cm (9½in) at birth, are born in early summer in British
seas, spring in the Mediterranean.
Range From Scotland and Denmark south to Morocco, and
throughout the Mediterranean.

Electric Ray
Torpedo nobiliana

Family name Torpedinidae (electric rays; torpedoes)
Length maximum 1.8m (6ft); width about 1.2m (4ft)
Weight maximum 43.5kg (96lb)

Identification Large fish with the body compressed from above to form an almost circular disc. Much of this width is comprised of the electric organs. Eyes very small; spiracles relatively large, smooth-edged; mouth on the underside of the disc, small but with pointed teeth. Tail fin broad and flat; the tail short and rounded in cross-section; dorsal fins small, the first only a little larger than the second. Coloration: deep brown to slate grey on the back; colour uniform and not mottled. The underside is pure white.
Habitat A bottom-living fish on mud or sand in depths of 10–150m (5½–82 fathoms). Migrates to cooler seas in summer; assumed to swim in mid-water some of the time.
Food A wide range of bottom-living or near-bottom-living fishes, which are stunned by an electric shock and then eaten.
Breeding Live-bearing, probably in early summer.
Range From Scotland and Denmark southwards to the Canary Islands; throughout the Mediterranean. Off eastern North America and in the southern Atlantic.

Torpedo
Torpedo torpedo

Family name Torpedinidae (electric rays; torpedos)
Length maximum about 60cm (24in); usually around
40cm (16in)

Identification Body and pectoral and pelvic fins compressed
from above to form a flat, fleshy disc which is almost circular,
but with the front edge flattened. Two relatively small dorsal
fins, the first only just larger than the second; the tail fin broad
and rounded. Eyes small, spiracles larger than eyes, their edges
with papillae of varying lengths. Coloration: plain light brown,
sometimes milk chocolate colour above, with five regularly
spaced, large, blue-centred eye spots on the body. Underside
cream to white in colour.
Habitat Bottom-living on sand or mud. Usually occurs close
inshore at depths of 3–70m (2–38 fathoms). Lies partially
buried in the sand, the edges of the disc obscured by particles
thrown up and resettled.
Food Mostly small fishes, which may partly be lured close to
investigate the eye spots, then stunned by electricity and eaten.
Also eats invertebrates.
Breeding Live-bearing, producing 3–20 young measuring
8–10cm (3.2–4in) during spring and summer.
Range Most abundant on the southern coast of the
Mediterranean but reported from northern Spain southwards
to the Canary Islands and Angola.

Blonde Ray

Raja brachyura

Family name Rajidae (rays and skates)
Length maximum about 1.13m (44in)
Weight maximum 17.12kg (37lb 7oz)

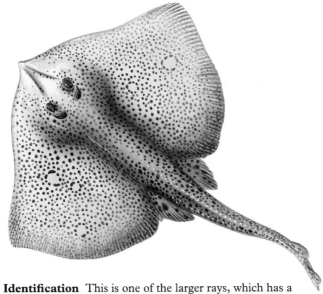

Identification This is one of the larger rays, which has a
rather short snout; the angles of the pectoral fins almost right-
angled. Adults have a line of large spines along the mid-line of
the tail (young have spines on the back as well). The skin of
the whole back and wings is prickly to touch. Coloration: the
back is light brown with larger creamy-white blotches, but
with the entire back and top of tail covered with dark
chocolate spots which extend to the edges of the fins. White
ventrally.
Habitat Bottom-living in coastal waters but not close
inshore. Most common on sandy and gravelly banks in depths
of 40m (22 fathoms), exceptionally to twice that depth.
Food Eats a wide range of crustaceans, worms and bottom-
living fishes, especially pouting, sandeels and sole.
Breeding Lays eggs in rectangular light brown cases with a
curved horn at each corner. Egg cases shed mostly in summer.
Range Scottish waters southwards to North Africa, and in the
northern part of the Mediterranean.

Thornback Ray or Roker
Raja clavata

Family name Rajidae (rays and skates)
Length maximum 85cm (34in) long, 60cm (24in) wide
Weight possibly up to 17.25kg (38lb)

Identification A ray with a right-angled pointed snout and
right-angled wings; the front edges of the disc are slightly
wavy. Adult specimens, particularly large females, have large
thorny spines in several rows up their tail on the back, and
scattered large thorns over the disc. Skin on back and top of
tail is rough with coarse prickles. Coloration: on the back
variable, usually medium brown to light brown with yellowish
patches. Numerous dark spots. Ventrally a pale cream colour.
Habitat The commonest ray in inshore waters, living on
muddy, sandy and gravel bottoms in depths of 10–60m
(5½–33 fathoms). The young live inshore in shallower depths.
Food When young, eats small crustaceans; as it grows, eats
crabs, shrimps and a large number of bottom-living fishes,
mainly sandeels, pouting and small flatfishes, as well as herring
and sprat.
Breeding Egg capsules are laid in shallow inshore water
during summer; they hatch in 4–5 months.
Range From northern Norway and southern Iceland south to
Morocco, throughout the Mediterranean and the Black Sea in
coastal waters.

Small-eyed Ray
Raja microocellata

Family name Rajidae (rays and skates)
Length maximum 82cm (32in) long, 60cm (24in) wide
Weight maximum 5.4kg (12lb)

Identification In this ray the angles of the wings are almost right angles, but the tips are curved; the snout is short. The eyes are comparatively small; the combined length from the front of the eye to the back of the spiracle is less than half the space between the eyes. The skin on the front half of the disc only is prickly; the back half is smooth. Larger spines run down the centre of the back and tail; they are close packed and bent over at right angles. Coloration: distinctive, greyish-brown to medium brown on the back, with indistinct creamy stripes which run more or less parallel to the edges of the fins. White ventrally.

Habitat Shallow water from close inshore down to depths of 100m (55 fathoms), particularly on sandy ground. Tends to favour some bays or sand banks in preference to others.

Food Bottom-living fishes and some invertebrates.

Breeding Eggs in brownish capsules 8–9cm (3¼–3¾in) long; mostly laid in summer.

Range Occurs mostly on the western coasts of Ireland and Wales and southern England, southwards to Gibraltar.

Spotted Ray
Raja montagui

Family name Rajidae (rays and skates)
Length maximum 75cm (30in) long, 51cm (20in) wide
Weight maximum 3.8kg (8lb 5oz)

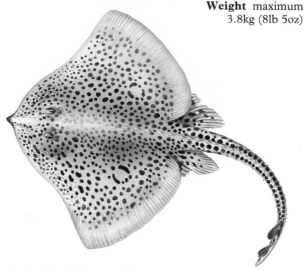

Identification In this ray the snout is short
and the outer angles of the wings are almost right-angled,
but the tips are rounded. The front edges of the disc are
sinuous. The skin on the back of the disc has fine prickles
along the front edge back to the level of the eyes in adults
(less far in the young); otherwise the skin is smooth. A mid-
line row of very close-packed spines runs along the disc and
tail. Irregular spines are present on the sides of the tail.
Coloration: warm brown on the back with numerous black
spots which do not extend to the very edge of the wings.
Habitat Lives in moderately deep water, mainly between
60–120m (33–66 fathoms) but occasionally much shallower
than this. Most common on sandy ground, but is occasionally
caught near rocks.
Food Eats crustaceans of various kinds, ranging from sand
hoppers and shrimps when young to crabs when adult.
Sometimes eats fishes.
Breeding Lays eggs in brown leathery capsules April–July in
shallow water. The capsule horns are all short.
Range From Scottish waters and the coast of the Netherlands
southwards to Gibraltar, and in the western Mediterranean.

Skate

Raja batis

Family name Rajidae (rays and skates)
Length maximum 2.8m (9ft 4in) females, 2m (6ft 6in) males
Weight maximum 103kg (227lb)

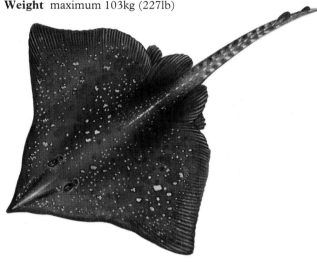

Identification One of several long-snouted skates in which
the snout length is more than twice the distance between the
eyes, but this is the only one common in inshore waters. The
front edges of the disc are strongly concave. Young fish are
smooth-skinned on the back, adult females have prickles on
the front edge of the disc but males are prickly all over. Both
sexes as adults have prickles on the underside. A row of 12–20
large spines along the mid-line of the tail. Coloration: dark
olive brown on the back with light brown blotches; ventrally
blue-grey or ash–grey with rows of black sensory pores.
Habitat Lives in deep water of 30–600m (16–328 fathoms)
but young fish live mainly in the shallower depths. Most
common on rocky grounds with clear patches of sand.
Food Eats fishes such as cod and haddock, and crustaceans.
Probably hunts well above the sea bed for some of its food.
Breeding Lays eggs February–August in rectangular capsules
15–25cm (6–10in) long and 8–15cm (3–6in) wide.
Range An uncommon fish, except on the open ocean coasts
of Scotland and Ireland. Occurs from northern Norway and
Iceland south to Madeira, and in the western Mediterranean.
Now much rarer than it once was because of overfishing.

Brown Ray
Raja miraletus

Family name Rajidae (rays and skates)
Length maximum 60cm (24in)

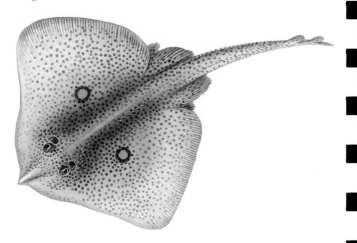

Identification A short-snouted ray in which the length of the snout (from front of eyes to tip of snout) is about 1½ times the width between the eyes. The tips of the wings are smoothly rounded but nearly right-angled. Upper surface of body prickly in young, nearly smooth in adults; ventral surface smooth at all sizes. A patch of larger spines on the front edge of the disc and another on the wings. Three broken rows of spines along the tail. Coloration: upper surface medium brown to reddish-brown densely covered with darker spots. A highly conspicuous circular eye spot on each wing, its centre light blue, surrounded by a deep blue ring which is surrounded by an orange outer ring.
Habitat Lives on the sea bed, mostly on sandy bottoms, at 10–300m (5.5–164 fathoms) but mostly at 50–150m (55–82 fathoms).
Food Eats a wide range of mostly bottom-living animals, including fishes, crustaceans and molluscs.
Breeding Eggs laid mostly April–August in rectangular cases which measure about 50 x 35mm (2 x 1.4in).
Range Occurs throughout the Mediterranean in suitable habitats and in the adjacent Atlantic from northern Portugal southwards to Madeira and the West African coast.

Cuckoo Ray
Raja naevus

Family name Rajidae (rays and skates)
Length maximum 70cm (28in)
Width maximum 2.7kg (5lb 11oz)

Identification This small ray is very distinct from most of the rays of northern Europe. Its snout is short, with the very tip protuberant and the wings rounded to form a smooth curve. The upper surface of the body is covered with fine prickles, except for a rounded patch on each wing; the underside is smooth but has prickles along the front edge. A patch of large spines in the middle of the disc just behind the eyes. A double row of curved, close-packed spines running along the mid-line of the back and the tail. Young specimens have spines on the mid-line of the body. Coloration: back grey-brown with light patches on the disc, and a very distinct, circular black and yellow mark on the middle of each wing.
Habitat A bottom-living ray found on sandy patches in fairly shallow water of 20–150m (11–80 fathoms).
Food When young eats all kinds of crustaceans and worms; as an adult eats fishes (herring, sandeels, members of the cod family and small flatfishes).
Breeding Eggs are laid mainly December–May. The rectangular egg capsule measures about 6 x 4cm (2½ x 1½in).
Range From Shetland and Denmark south to Gibraltar, and in the western Mediterranean. Moderately common to the south and west of the British Isles.

Undulate Ray
Raja undulata

Family name Rajidae (rays and skates)
Length maximum 1.2m (4ft); British specimens are smaller
Weight maximum 9.6kg
(21lb 4oz)

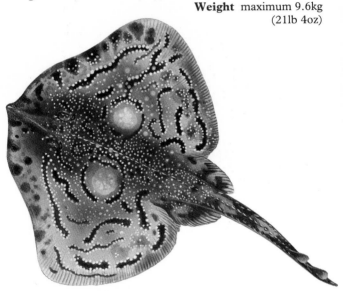

Identification The pectoral fins are rounded, as is the snout, although the tip of the snout is protuberant. The snout is covered with coarse prickles ventrally, but the rest of the underside is bare. The back is prickly, except for the rear edges of the pectoral and pelvic fins. A series of larger spines down the mid-line of the back and tail and irregular rows of spines on each side of the tail. Coloration: yellowish-brown to deep brown on the back, with distinct, wavy dark lines margined with white or yellow spots. White ventrally.
Habitat Lives on sandy bottoms in inshore waters at 45–100m (25–55 fathoms), occasionally deeper.
Food Mainly eats fishes, particularly flatfish, gobies and dragonets, and squids and crustaceans.
Breeding The eggs are laid within opaque, reddish-brown capsules 8.5–5cm (3.2–2in) long, mainly in summer in northern seas, in spring in the Mediterranean.
Range From southern England and Ireland (where rare), through the western Mediterranean down to southern Africa.

Stingray
Dasyatis pastinaca

Family name
Dasyatidae
(stingrays)

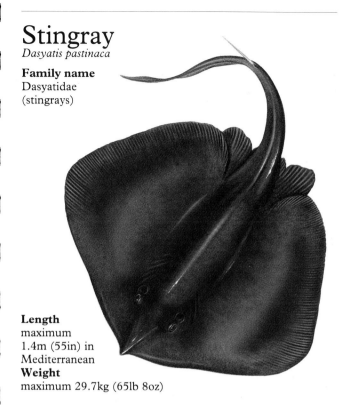

Length
maximum
1.4m (55in) in
Mediterranean
Weight
maximum 29.7kg (65lb 8oz)

Identification Unique in northern European seas, where it is the only true stingray, but in the Mediterranean there are three other species. Pectoral fins produced laterally to form huge rounded wings; the pelvics are small. Eyes moderately large, as are spiracles. No dorsal fin but there is one, sometimes two or three, long, serrated and dangerous envenomed spines about halfway down the tail. The tail continues as a long, thin whiplash. Coloration: greyish or olive brown, occasionally with light patches. Ventrally cream coloured with grey edges.
Habitat Lives on soft bottoms of sand or mud in depths of 3.7–73m (2–40 fathoms). Most commonly found in coastal waters, particularly in sheltered estuaries.
Food Exclusively bottom-living organisms, especially crabs, other crustaceans and molluscs.
Breeding Gives birth to well-developed young, 6–9 at a time, mostly in summer, but may not breed in north European seas.
Range From northern Scotland and Denmark southwards, throughout the Mediterranean and south to southern Africa.

Eagle Ray
Myliobatis aquila

Family name
Myliobatidae
(eagle-rays)

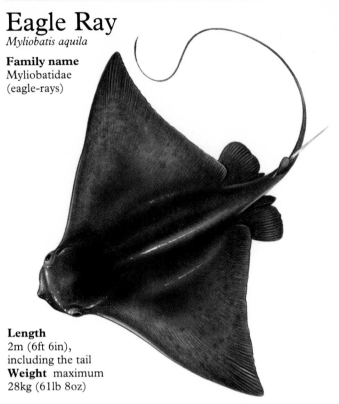

Length
2m (6ft 6in),
including the tail
Weight maximum
28kg (61lb 8oz)

Identification The pectoral fins are expanded laterally into large wings, almost pointed at their tips, which run smoothly into the distinct head. Pelvic fins relatively small. Dorsal fin small, sited near the base of the tail. Just posterior to the dorsal fin is a serrated, pointed and envenomed spine. Tail long and whip-like. Eyes lateral, followed by a large spiracle on each side. Coloration: grey-brown on the back, sometimes with bronze tints. Ventrally creamy-white with grey edges.
Habitat Spends part of its time on the sea bed but more often swims strongly in mid-water or near the surface. Mainly found in inshore waters down to 100m (55 fathoms).
Food Hard-shelled invertebrates such as molluscs and crustaceans. Its flattened, broad teeth help in crushing shells.
Breeding Live-bearing; litters of up to seven are born mainly in summer. Not known to breed in northern waters.
Range Occasional records from southern Sweden, Denmark and south to Morocco; throughout the Mediterranean.

Sturgeon
Acipenser sturio

Family name Acipenseridae (sturgeons)
Length maximum 3.5m (11ft 6in); rarely more than 2.5m (8ft 3in)

Identification Characteristic body shape with the tail asymetric and five rows of bony plates on the back, sides and belly. Snout bluntly pointed; barbels close to mouth, not fringed. 24–40 bony plates in rows on sides. Coloration: dark greeny-brown above, fading to yellowish on sides; creamy-white ventrally.
Habitat Although the sturgeon breeds in fresh waters, much of its life is spent in the sea. It is mainly a bottom-dwelling, shallow-water fish, but it migrates for hundreds of miles to suitable feeding grounds. It must be assumed to swim in mid-water while migrating.
Food In the sea it eats molluscs, polychaete worms, crustaceans and bottom-living fishes, mostly animals which would burrow in sand or mud.
Breeding In spring in rivers. The eggs are buried in gravel.
Range Ostensibly the sturgeon ranges from northern Norway and southern Iceland southwards to Gibraltar and in the northern Mediterranean and Black Sea. In fact, the only breeding populations on the Atlantic coast are in the Gironde in France. The stocks in the Guadalquivir, Rhone and Po are now virtually extinct.

Eel
Anguilla anguilla

Family name Anguillidae (freshwater eel)
Length 50cm (20in) males; 1m (39in) females
Weight maximum 58kg (11lb)

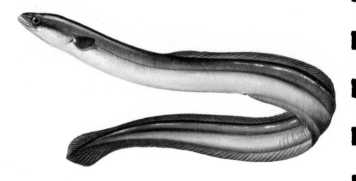

Identification Distinctively eel-like, elongate body with long dorsal and anal fins meeting at the tail. Dorsal fin origin about one third of the way along the body; pectoral fins rounded. Lower jaw protuberant, longer than the upper jaw. Gill slits small, just in front of pectoral fin. Coloration: variable with habitat; often brownish on the back, yellow on the sides. Maturing eels are black on the back, silvery on the belly (these are very rarely seen in the sea).
Habitat Freshwater eels mainly live in the sea at two phases of their lives – as maturing fish migrating to their spawning ground, and as post-larvae and elvers. This last stage is most abundant and they may be found as 10-cm (4-in) elvers on shores and in estuaries. A substantial number stay on the shore, buried in crevices, and grow to full size. Many live on rocky shores.
Food As young fish on the shore they eat crustaceans and small fishes; the post-larval stages eat planktonic animals; maturing eels do not feed.
Breeding Believed to be in mid-Atlantic. The young fish take three years to reach western Europe, four to reach Greece.
Range From northern Norway and Iceland south to Morocco and throughout the Mediterranean. Also in rivers leading to these seas.

Conger
Conger conger

Family name Congridae (conger eels)
Length maximum about 2.75m (9ft)
Weight 65kg (143lb)

Identification A large marine eel with elongate dorsal and anal fins which fuse in the region of the tail fin. The pectoral fins are rather pointed in outline, but in large specimens they tend to wear to a rounded shape. The dorsal fin originates just behind the end of the pectoral fin. The head is rather broad, the eyes large and the gill openings wide. Body scaleless, skin with heavy mucus. Coloration: dull brown to grey on the back, sharply set off against the lighter belly. Deep-water fish tend to be grey with dark edges on the fins.
Habitat From shore pools down to 183m (100 fathoms) and more. Generally those in shallow water are rather small. Always found on rocks, reefs, wrecks and around pier pilings.
Food Mostly bottom-living fishes, crabs and octopuses. They are not specialists, so will eat anything of appropriate size.
Breeding Is believed to breed in the tropical Atlantic at depths of 3000–4000m (1640–2200 fathoms), but detailed information is sparse. The post-larvae live at the surface and are transparent and willow-leaf shaped.
Range Along the European coastline from Iceland and mid-Norway to Morocco and the Mediterranean.

Moray
Muraena helena

Family name Muraenidae (moray eels)
Length maximum about 1.3m (51in), mostly much smaller

Identification Eel-like in body shape wlth very long dorsal and anal fins meeting at the tip of the tail. The dorsal fin origin is close behind the back of the head. No pectoral or pelvic fins; small, slit-like gill openings high on the side behind the head. The body is comparatively deep and compressed from side to side. Teeth in jaws dagger sharp. Coloration: dark brown or plum coloured on the back and sides with yellow mottling, less distinct towards the head.

Habitat Lives in crevices among rocks, rubble, shipwrecks and sunken amphorae. Found on the shore down to 30m (16½ fathoms). Active mainly at night.

Food Eats a wide range of fishes and cephalopods (squids and octopuses). Food details are little known.

Breeding Very poorly understood. Is believed to spawn in the summer, probably offshore. Has typical eel post-larva, transparent and laterally flattened.

Range Very rarely recorded as far north as the British Isles. Common on the Portuguese coast, Madeira and throughout the Mediterranean.

Note Moray eels should be handled with care; even small ones bite and the wound can become septic.

Herring
Clupea harengus

Family name Clupeidae (herrings)
Length maximum 43cm (17in), often much smaller
Weight maximum 450gm (1lb)

Identification Flat-sided with the belly forming a sharp edge, although rounded ventrally between the pectoral and pelvic fins. The scales are large and fragile, very easily detached. Dorsal fin origin is in front of or above the pelvic fin origin. Lower jaw prominent; no notch in the mid-line of the upper jaw. 13–15 sharply pointed scales between the pelvic fins and the vent. Coloration: back deep blue, lightening on the sides to silver-white on the belly. The sides of head and body gleam with golden tints.
Habitat A schooling, open-water fish which lives near the surface or in mid-water. Although most common offshore, in coastal waters it can be common on the coast. The young are particuarly abundant in estuarine conditions.
Food A plankton feeder, eating huge quantities of planktonic crustaceans, fish larvae and the floating young of other animals.
Breeding Lays its eggs in dense mats, often several layers thick, on the sea bed. Different races spawn in spring inshore or offshore in summer and autumn. The same spawning grounds are used year after year.
Range North Atlantic from northern Norway to northern Spain, Iceland, southern Greenland and along the Atlantic coast of North America.

Sprat

Sprattus sprattus

Family name Clupeidae (herrings)
Length maximum 16.5cm (6½in); mostly around
12.7cm (5in)

Identification Very similar to the young herring, with
flattened sides but with a sharp-toothed belly. The scales on
the ridge on the belly form a toothed keel; there are 11–12
teeth between the pelvic fins and the vent. The origin of the
dorsal fin is behind the base of the pelvics. Lower jaw just
prominent; no notch in the mid-line of the upper jaw; no
radiating ridges on the gill covers. Coloration: dark green on
the back and upper sides; brilliant silver on the lower sides
and belly.
Habitat An abundant inshore fish in the coastal waters of
northern Europe. Particularly common in estuaries and bays
over sandy bottoms, but found near the surface and in mid-
water in depths of 10–50m (5½–27 fathoms). They come
closer to the surface at night.
Food A plankton feeder, which eats large quantities of small
crustaceans (copepods), and crustacean and fish larvae.
Breeding Spawning takes place in spring and summer. The
eggs and larvae are planktonic, and the young fish drift inshore
as they grow.
Range From northern Norway southwards to Gibraltar, and
thence on the northern coasts of the Mediterranean and the
Black Sea.

Pilchard
Sardina pilchardus

Family name Clupeidae (herrings)
Length maximum 25cm (10in), very rarely larger
Weight maximum 225g (8oz)

Identification Clearly a member of the herring family, with a single dorsal fin, deeply forked tail and large, easily dislodged scales. However, the body is plumper and the belly more rounded, with at most a very faint ridge along the mid-line. Origin of dorsal fin is in front of the pelvic fin base. The lower jaw is almost equal in length to the upper jaw. The gill covers are deeply ridged with radiating lines. The last rays of the anal fin are slightly longer than the remainder and stand out from the fin outline. Coloration: back blue-green shading to gold on the sides, silver ventrally; a dusky patch just behind the head.
Habitat A pelagic schooling fish, living at 27–55m (15–30 fathoms) but moving up towards the surface at night. Strongly migratory into northern and inshore waters during the summer. It is affected by ocean circulation and temperature, tending to become rare after years of abundance in places.
Food Eats plankton, the eggs and young of crustaceans, particularly copepods, as well as the adults.
Breeding Spawning takes place in spring and summer at the surface in offshore waters. The young fish are pelagic and move inshore to overwinter.
Range From southern Norway and Scotland southwards to the Canary Islands, in the Mediterranean and the Black Sea.

Twaite Shad
Alosa fallax

Family name Clupeidae (herrings)
Length maximum 55cm (22in)
Weight maximum 1.4kg (3lb 2oz)

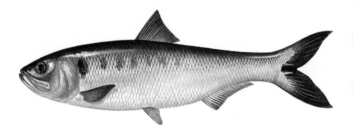

Identification A large, heavy-bodied, large-headed fish which is clearly a relative of the herring from its general appearance. It has a single dorsal fin, the origin of which is just in front of the pelvic fins. The sides are compressed and the belly is deep, but with a sharply-toothed keel along its mid-line. The upper jaw has a notch in the mid-line, into which the lower jaw slots. The gill covers have weak radiating ridges. Gill rakers, on the inner side of the first gill arch under the gill cover, number 40–60 (fewer and shorter than the red gills). Coloration: brilliant deep blue above fading to golden yellow on the sides. There is a line of 6–8 blotches on the sides behind the head.

Habitat A rare migratory fish which in the sea is most common in coastal waters and in estuaries. It travels in schools near the surface.

Food Mostly swimming crustaceans and small fishes such as sandeels, sprats and young herring.

Breeding Ascends rivers to spawn in late spring; enters estuaries a month or two earlier.

Range Notionally from southern Iceland and the Baltic Sea southwards to Morocco and throughout the Mediterranean but now so rare (due to pollution and obstructions of spawning rivers) that it is a threatened species in all Europe.

Anchovy

Engraulis encrasicolus

Family name Engraulidae (anchovies)
Length maximum 20cm (8in); usually 9–12cm (3¼–4¾in)

Identification A slender-bodied fish which is rounded in cross-section, with no keel on the belly. The snout is pointed and protuberant, with the lower jaw entirely overhung and very long, reaching back well behind the level of the rear of the eye. Body scales large and fragile, easily detached. Coloration: clear green on the back, sides bright silver with a golden tinge on the gill covers; silvery-white ventrally.

Habitat A fish which forms enormous schools in the surface waters of the sea. Migratory, moving northwards in summer entering estuaries and sea bights, and offshore with the onset of winter. The North Sea stocks probably migrate from the southern part of the western English Channel.

Food A planktonic feeder which eats small crustaceans and young fishes in great quantities. The huge lower jaw swings down from the upper jaw to create a scoop bounded by a fine network of gill rakers within.

Breeding Eggs are laid June–August at the surface and float until they hatch. The larvae and young fish are also pelagic.

Range From Denmark and Scotland southwards to West Africa; throughout the Mediterranean and the Black Sea.

Salmon
Salmo salar

Family name Salmonidae (salmons and trouts)
Length 1.5m (5ft)
Weight rarely to 36kg (80lb)

Identification Large fishes with an adipose fin. Body
rounded, but with rather compressed sides; caudal peduncle
(tail fin stalk) narrow. The tail fin rays stand out from the
outline above and below; the tail fin is shallowly forked. Upper
jawbone extends to the level of the back of the eye, not
beyond. Coloration: in the sea all salmon will be green or blue
on the back, silver-sided and silvery-white beneath. The larger
ones have small, x-shaped spots on their sides.
Habitat Young salmon live in the sea from the ages of 3–7
years, by which time they are quite large. They migrate
downriver from their spawning grounds, then feed in the
estuary and coastal waters before making distant migrations, in
some cases to the Norwegian Sea, in others to Greenland.
They live mostly near the surface or in mid-water.
Food Mostly crustaceans and small fishes, principally herring
family and sandeels. The distant-water migrants feed mostly
on shrimp-like animals.
Breeding Adults return to the river of their birth to spawn,
mostly in summer to early winter, spawning in mid-winter in
gravel near the headwaters of streams.
Range A North Atlantic species ranging from the Arctic
region of the USSR to northern Spain, and from Greenland
down the coasts of Canada and the United States. Now
greatly reduced in number due to pollution, obstructions in
rivers and overfishing.

Smelt
Osmerus eperlanus

Family name Osmeridae (smelts)
Length maximum 30cm (12in), mostly much smaller
Weight maximum 190g (6oz)

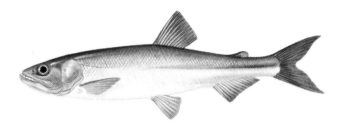

Identification The smelt has the general body plan of the salmons and trouts, being relatively slender but rounded in cross-section. It has a single rayed dorsal fin and an adipose (rayless) fin on the back. The mouth is very wide, with long jaws which have strong curved teeth. Identification is confirmed by its heavy smell of cucumber. Coloration: light olive brown on the back, the underside creamy white; the sides are light olive with an indistinct silvery stripe.

Habitat Lives in schools in estuaries and in shallow, inshore waters. Enters rivers in spring on its way to upstream spawning grounds.

Breeding Spawns in spring in rivers near the upstream limit of saltwater flow. The eggs are laid in gravel, but break free to float in the surface waters until hatching. Young fish live near the surface.

Food For its size it is a fierce predator. It eats large numbers of young herring and sprat, and crustaceans. Young fish eat planktonic crustaceans.

Range From the White Sea to France, but mostly in isolated populations clustered near large river mouths. Some live entirely in freshwater lakes.

Cod
Gadus morhua

Family name Gadidae (codfishes)
Length maximum about 1.5m (5ft); usually about 1.2m (4ft)
Weight maximum about 45.5kg (100lb)

Identification A stout-bodied fish with a large head and a well-developed chin barbel. Like many members of its family, it has three dorsal and two anal fins; the pelvic fins are small but with a long first ray. All the dorsal fins are rounded in outline; the first anal fin origin is beneath the space between first and second dorsal fins or just behind this. Upper jaw overhangs the lower jaw. Coloration: back olive brown or greenish, occasionally dark brown; sides lighter, mottled; white ventrally. The lateral line is light.

Habitat Young cod live just below low-tide mark down to 20m (11 fathoms); adults live from the latter depth to 80m (44 fathoms) and deeper. They form schools which gather a few metres above the sea bed, although when feeding they hunt on the bottom.

Breeding Spawns February–April in water of 200m (109 fathoms) or thereabouts. The eggs are shed in mid-water and are distributed by the ocean currents. The adults make long migrations to reach specific spawning grounds.

Food Eats an enormous range of mostly bottom-living fishes and invertebrates.

Range From Arctic USSR south to Biscay and across the Atlantic to Newfoundland, Greenland and the eastern seaboard of North America.

Haddock
Melanogrammus aeglefinus

Family name Gadidae (codfishes)
Length exceptionally 1.1m (44in); usually around
64cm (25in)
Weight maximum 6kg (13lb 11oz)

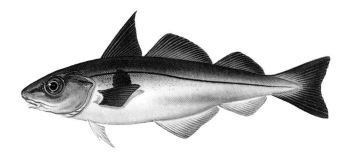

Identification Typical codfish body shape with three dorsal
and two anal fins and the body extending into the tail fin in
characteristic fashion. The first dorsal fin is relatively high and
pointed in outline. Pelvic fins small with the first rays elongate.
Head rather small, eyes large; the lower jaw short so that the
mouth is ventral; a short barbel on the chin. Coloration: dark
greeny-brown above, greyish-silver on the sides, white
ventrally. The lateral line is black. A conspicuous dark thumb
print on the side above the pectoral fin base.
Habitat A schooling fish which lives close to the sea bed in
depths of 40–300m (22–164 fathoms). Occasionally it is
caught close inshore in shallower water than this. Migratory,
in the north of its range it comes closer to shore in winter; to
the south it is found in shallow inshore water in winter.
Breeding Spawning takes place mainly during March–April
in mid-water. The eggs and newly hatched young live near the
surface. Young haddock often accompany large, surface-living
jellyfishes, living among their tentacles.
Food A wide range of bottom-living animals, mainly
brittlestars, worms, molluscs and even sponges. It also eats
small fishes (sandeels and capelin).
Range North Atlantic from northern Norway to the English
Channel, and on the Atlantic coast of North America.

Whiting
Merlangius merlangus

Family name Gadidae (codfishes)
Length exceptionally to 70cm (28in); usually to 40cm (16in)
Weight maximum 3kg (6lb 12oz)

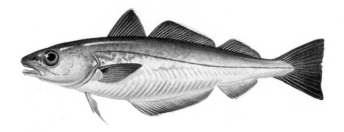

Identification A slender-bodied codfish with three dorsal
fins and two anal fins; all the fins are joined together at their
bases. The origin of the anal fin is beneath the first dorsal fin.
Pelvic fins small, the first rays elongate. The upper jaw is
slightly longer than the lower, mouth large, no chin barbel
except in small fish in which it is minute. Coloration: back
sandy to greeny-blue, the sides and belly silvery when alive.
A distinct black spot at the base of the pectoral fin.
Habitat Very common in shallow inshore water, particularly
over sand, mud and gravel. The species ranges from depths of
2m (6ft 6in) to 200m (109 fathoms), but usually only the
smaller fish live in very shallow water. Young fish of about
3cm (1¼in) are often seen sheltering under the tentacles of
live jellyfishes and sometimes drift inshore with their host.
Breeding Spawning takes place mostly in spring in shallow
water inshore and at depths up to 150m (82 fathoms). The
eggs and young larvae are planktonic.
Food Large whiting eat fishes, particularly sandeels, young
herring and sprats, other members of the cod family and
crustaceans. Young ones eat more crustaceans than fishes.
Range European seas, from northern Norway and Iceland
southwards to Gibraltar along the northern coast of the
Mediterranean to the Black Sea.

Bib

Trisopterus luscus

Family name Gadidae (codfishes)
Length maximum about 41cm (16¼in); usually around 30cm (12in)
Weight maximum 2.5kg (5lb 8oz)

Identification A typical codfish with three dorsal fins and two anal fins. The bases of the dorsal and the anal fins overlap, and the first anal fin rays are beneath the middle of the first dorsal. Pelvic fins with very long first rays which reach beyond the first anal rays. The body is deep and the sides of the fish are slightly compressed. Eyes are large; it has a long chin barbel. Coloration: coppery brown on the back, golden or yellowish on the sides and white ventrally. Four or five dusky bands across the sides, a bold black spot at the base of the pectoral fins.
Habitat Very common in inshore waters from 3–300m (1½–164 fathoms). The smallest fish live only in very shallow water. Small bib are abundant on sandy bottoms in shallow water, but larger specimens are most common over rocky reefs and wrecks, where they form small dispersed schools.
Breeding Spawns in spring in northern Europe and in winter in the Mediterranean. The eggs and young fish are pelagic.
Food Mainly crustaceans, particularly amphipods, shrimps and small crabs; also eats squids and small fishes.
Range From southern Norway south to Morocco and on the northern coastline of the western Mediterranean. Very common in the North Sea and the English Channel.

Pollack
Pollachius pollachius

Family name Gadidae (codfishes)
Length maximum 1.3m (51in); usually around
50cm (19½in)
Weight maximum 13.2kg (29lb 4oz)

Identification Typical of the cod family, with three dorsal
fins and two anal fins; all the fins are well spaced from one
another. The jaws are unequal; the lower jaw protrudes
beyond the upper jaw; there is no chin barbel. The lateral line
is curved in a gentle arc above the pectoral fin. Coloration:
dull greenish-brown on the back, shading to yellowish-green
on the sides, dull white ventrally. The lateral line is dark.
Habitat Widely distributed in European waters. Large fish
are most common in small schools over rocky reefs and wrecks
down to a depth of 200m (109 fathoms). Smaller specimens
can be caught over sandy bottoms in shallow water but they
are more abundant in the proximity of rocks.
Breeding Spawns January–April in deep water at 100–200m
(55–109 fathoms). Eggs and larvae are pelagic and drift
inshore as the larvae grow. The first- and second-year young
are found close to the shore.
Food Eats mostly fishes (sandeels, sprats, small codfish family
members) and squids. Young ones eat large numbers of
crustaceans.
Range European seas from northern Norway and Iceland
southwards to Morocco and on the northern coast of the
western Mediterranean basin. Particularly common on the
western and southern coasts of the British Isles.

Saithe
Pollachius virens

Family name Gadidae (codfishes)
Length maximum 1.3m (51in); mostly around 70cm (28in)
Weight maximum 17kg (37lb 5oz)

Identification Similar to the pollack and again with the
typical cod family features of three dorsal and two anal fins, all
being well spaced from one another. The jaws are more or less
equal in size, but in the largest fish the lower jaw is slightly
longer than the upper. No chin barbel, but it is minute in
juveniles. The lateral line is straight from the edge of the gill
cover to the tail. Coloration: dark browny-green on the back
and upper sides; lower sides and belly silvery-grey, sharply
differentiated from the back coloration. Lateral line cream
coloured.
Habitat Of wide distribution in the North Atlantic. Often
associated with rocky grounds or wrecks, although large
numbers live in open water above sand or gravel bottoms in
the north of its range. Young ones (1–2 years old) live in shore
pools among algae and in a metre or two of water. Very large
specimens live around wrecks and reefs.
Breeding Spawns January–April in depths of 100–200m
(55–108 fathoms) offshore. The eggs and larvae are pelagic
and drift into shallower water as they develop.
Food Young fish eat crustaceans and young fishes. Larger
saithe eat fishes very extensively (sandeels, herring, small
members of the codfish family).
Range Both sides of the northern North Atlantic (in North
America it is called pollock), from northern Norway and
Iceland southwards to the English Channel

Five-bearded Rockling

Ciliata mustela

Family name Gadidae (codfishes)
Length maximum 25cm (10in)
Weight maximum 180g (6oz)

Identification A slender-bodied codfish, almost eel-like in
appearance, with a short first dorsal fin which is entirely made
up of fine, hair-like rays (with one longer, thicker ray in the
front) and a long-based second dorsal fin similar in shape to
the anal fin, which is a little shorter. Pelvic fins small, with
elongate first rays. Five barbels on the front of the head, a pair
on the edge of the nostrils, another pair on the front of the
upper lip, and the fifth on the underside of the chin. Edge of
the upper lip smooth. Coloration: dark brown above,
sometimes reddish; light-grey and mottled below.

Habitat Mostly captured between tide marks on rocky
shores, but also in breakwater pools (provided there is algae in
them) on sandy shores. Also lives down to 20m (11 fathoms).
Hides under rocks or seaweed.

Breeding Spawns in winter and early spring offshore, the
eggs and early young being pelagic. Juvenile rocklings are
silvery with greenish backs and live at the surface before
adopting a shore habitat.

Food Small crustaceans, worms and small fishes.

Range From northern Norway and southern Iceland
southwards to the Portuguese coast. Abundant on rocky
shores in the British Isles.

Four-bearded Rockling

Enchelyopus cimbrius

Family name Gadidae (codfishes)
Length maximum about 40cm (16in); usually around
25cm (10in)

Identification Slender-bodied and almost eel-like with a
long-based second dorsal fin, a little longer than the anal fin,
but both low. First dorsal fin short, comprised of low, hair-like
rays with a very long thicker first fin ray. Snout rounded and
eyes large. Four barbels around the head, one on each anterior
nostril, one in the mid-line of the upper lip, and one on the
chin. Coloration: usually sandy coloured or light brown above,
grey on the sides, white ventrally; a rounded black blotch on
the posterior end of both dorsal and anal fins.
Habitat Never abundant but most common on sandy or
muddy grounds. It lives in burrows created in the bottom,
emerging to feed mostly at night or in the half-light. Lives at
depths of 10–250m (5½–137 fathoms).
Breeding Spawns in deep water in late spring and summer.
The eggs and larvae are pelagic, but the young fish begin to
live near the sea bed when 8–10cm (3–4in) long.
Food Feeds mainly on crustaceans, worms and other
invertebrates; large fish eat bottom-living fishes.
Range Lives both sides of the North Atlantic, in the east
from northern Norway and Iceland to the English Channel; is
definitely more abundant in the north of its range.

Shore Rockling
Gaidropsarus mediterraneus

Family name Gadidae (codfishes)
Length maximum 40cm (16in)
Weight maximum 595g (1lb 5oz)

Identification Slender-bodied, almost eel-like in shape, with a long-based, low second dorsal fin only slightly lower than the similar anal fin. The first dorsal fin is composed of fine hair-like rays with a longer ray in front of the fin. Pelvic fins small, the first rays elongated and thickened. Pectoral fin rounded with 15–17 rays. Three barbels on the head – one on each anterior nostril and one on the tip of the lower jaw.
Coloration: uniform dull brown or reddish-brown on the back and sides; lighter ventrally, often mottled.
Habitat A fish which lives on rocks from mid-shore down to a depth of 27m (15 fathoms). It hides in crevices under rocks or among the algae growing on the rocks, but is active during high tide.
Breeding Spawns offshore in deeper water in early summer, the eggs being pelagic, as are the early larvae. Later the young fish come inshore and are clear blue on the back and brilliant silver ventrally. They can be caught along the shoreline from September to October at a length of 4cm (1½in).
Food Mainly small crustaceans, amphipods and small shore crabs, small worms and young fishes. The young are eaten by a wide range of sea birds.
Range From mid-Norway south to Gibraltar and throughout the northern Mediterranean and western Black Sea. Only abundant on rocky shores.

Three-bearded Rockling
Gaidropsarus vulgaris

Family name Gadidae (codfishes)
Length maximum 53cm (21in); mostly about 40cm (16in)
Weight maximum 1.4kg (3lb 2oz)

Identification Relatively slender-bodied but with a broad head and anterior body. The head is also rather long. Second dorsal fin uniform in height and rather low, only a little longer than the anal fin. First dorsal fin composed of fine, hair-like rays with a larger, longer ray in front. Pelvic fins rather small, but with the anterior rays long and rather fleshy. Pectoral fins broad, rounded, with 20–22 branched rays. Three barbels: one on each nostril, the third under the centre of the lower jaw. Coloration: pale sandy brown or salmon pink with bold, dark brown bars and blotches on the back and sides.
Habitat Lives among rocks and around wrecks, often in seaweed, at depths of 9–50m (5–27 fathoms). Never found between tide marks. It is also found on gravel or sand patches between rocky outcrops.
Breeding Spawns in winter (January–February). The eggs and early larvae are pelagic and the juveniles have clear green backs and brilliant silvery sides like the young of other rocklings.
Food Eats mainly crustaceans but also takes smaller, bottom-living fishes.
Range From the coast of Norway and Scotland southwards to Gibraltar and in the western basin of the Mediterranean. Most common around the British Isles.

Ling
Molva molva

Family name Gadidae (codfishes)
Length 2m (6ft 6in); in inshore waters about 1.5m (5ft)
Weight maximum 27kg (59lb 8oz)

Identification A relatively large member of the cod family,
which shares the long-bodied shape of the rocklings but is a lot
bigger. The first dorsal fin is small and rounded in outline,
having 14–15 normal rays in it. The second dorsal fin is long-
based and of uniform height, and only a little longer than the
anal fin. Pectoral and pelvic fins small. Head large but narrow,
with a large mouth equipped with long teeth. Lower jaw equal
or a little shorter than upper jaw; a long chin barbel is present.
Coloration: dull browny-grey, mottled on the back, lighter
below. A dark spot on the rear edge of the first dorsal fin;
similar blotches on the end of the second dorsal and anal fins.
Habitat A moderately deep-water fish, living at 50–400m
(27–219 fathoms). Most common near rocky grounds and
around wrecks, and lives in hiding in crevices. In deep water it
seems to be free-swimming.
Breeding Spawns March–July over deep water. Amazingly
fecund, a single large female may lay up to 60 million eggs.
The eggs and early larvae float near the surface.
Food Eats mainly fishes (other members of the cod family)
and crustaceans.
Range From northern Norway southwards to Biscay;
common off the west coast of Britain. Other species occur to
the north or south; all three can be caught to the west of
Ireland.

Tadpole-fish

Raniceps raninus

Family name Ranicipiteridae (tadpole-fishes)
Length maximum 30cm (12in); mostly about half of this
Weight maximum 616g (1lb 5oz)

Identification A very stout-bodied, broad-headed fish which looks very silmilar to a large tadpole. The head is about as broad as it is long, the mouth wide and gaping when opened. Eyes relatively large. A small barbel on the chin. Two dorsal fins, the first tiny (three small rays) widely separated from the second fin. Second dorsal long-based and low, only a little longer than the similarly shaped anal fin. Pectoral fins broad and rounded; pelvic fin small but rather long. Coloration: uniform dark above, varying from deep chocolate brown to plum coloured; ventrally greyish. The mouth and lips are white, edges of the fins light.

Habitat A solitary shallow-water fish which lives on the sea bed close to rocks and algae-covered hard structures. In northern regions it lives from the lower shore down to 100m (55 fathoms) but in the south it lives in deeper water. It occasionally occurs on sandy or muddy bottoms.

Breeding Spawns in late summer and early autumn, usually inshore. The eggs and larvae are very small and pelagic, but the young live on the sea bed once they reach the length of about 2cm (¾in).

Food Mostly shrimps and worms; occasionally small fishes.

Range Occurs from northern Norway south to the Brittany peninsula; it seems most common on the western coasts of the British Isles.

Hake
Merluccius merluccius

Family name Merluciidae (hakes)
Length maximum 1.8m (6ft), but rarely over 1m (39in)
Weight maximum about 11.5kg (25lb 5oz)

Identification A slim-bodied fish with a large head and big
jaws which are liberally equipped with long, curved teeth. Two
dorsal fins, the first high and triangular but short-based, the
second long-based and almost equal in length to the anal fin.
The outline of these fins dips about two-thirds along. Tail fin
well developed with square-cut edges. Body scales moderate
but easily detached. The lateral line straight. Coloration: blue-
grey on the back, silver on the sides, silvery-white ventrally.
Inside mouth and gill cavity the skin is black.
Habitat A moderately deep-water fish which lives on the
lower continental shelf at depths of 165–550m (90–300
fathoms) but which comes nearer the surface at night, and in
shallower water in the warm season. Hake are schooling fishes
which live off the sea bed in mid-water.
Breeding Spawns in spring and summer at depths of around
200m (109 fathoms). Eggs and larvae are pelagic and may
drift into shallower water.
Food Mainly fishes and squids, but also large quantities of
crustaceans.
Range Widely distributed in European seas, from Norway
and Iceland southwards to Morocco and throughout the
Mediterranean. Heavily overfished, the hake is now
comparatively scarce and is rarely caught in shallow water as it
once was.

Viviparous Blenny

Zoarces viviparus

Family name Zoarcidae (eelpouts)
Length maximum 50cm (19½in); usually around 30cm (12in)

Identification Long-bodied and almost eel-like, except that the head is broad and the abdominal region swollen. Lips very thick, eyes moderately large. Dorsal fin origin just above the back of the head, long and uniform in height except towards the tail, where the outline dips and there is a series of short spines. Dorsal, tail and anal fins continuous. Pectoral fins large and flap-like; pelvics two short stubs. Skin with deeply embedded scales. Coloration: dull greeny-brown on the back and sides, with an irregular series of dusky bars; yellowish ventrally.
Habitat Bottom-living, it is most common buried in mud or among rocks on a muddy shore and under algae. It is often common in estuaries. Lives on the shore from mid-tide level to 40m (22 fathoms).
Breeding A live-bearing fish. Mating takes place August–September. The eggs develop and hatch within the female and then continue to grow within the ovary. The young, which are miniatures of the adults, are born December–February at a length of 4cm (1½in).
Food Eats small crustaceans, molluscs and fishes.
Range Occurs from the White Sea around the Norwegian coast, throughout the Baltic and on the northern and eastern coasts of the British Isles.

Angler

Lophius piscatorius

Family name Lophiidae (angler-fishes)
Length maximum about 2m (6ft 6in);
uncommon above 1.2m (4ft)
Weight maximum 43kg (94lb 12oz)

Identification Highly distinctive, with a massive head of
rounded, flattened shape running into the tail, which is
rounded in cross-section. The mouth is broad, opening to an
enormous gape, and has massive, long teeth. The head and
body are outlined with small flaps of skin. A series of separate
rays in the mid-line of the head and anterior body; these form
the first dorsal fin. The second dorsal fin is normal in shape
with 11–12 fleshy rays. A pair of spines on the side of the head
just above the pectoral fin. No flap of skin above the eye.
Coloration: very variable on the back, from reddish-brown to
black, with dusky markings; ventrally pure white.
Habitat Bottom-living in depths of 2–548m (6½–300
fathoms). Lives on sand, shell and gravel bottoms in which it is
concealed by its coloration and the small flaps of skin around
the body's edge. Feeds by waving the first dorsal spine,
wriggling the flap of skin at its tip to attract prey.
Breeding Spawns spring–early summer. The eggs form a
massive, ribbon-like, gelatinous sheet near the surface. Larvae
are free-swimming but with hugely elongated fin rays.
Food Virtually any smaller fish attracted by the angler's lure.
Range From northern Norway southwards at least to West
Africa and throughout the Mediterranean. Common on the
coasts of the British Isles.

Black-bellied Angler

Lophius budegassa

Family name Lophiidae (angler-fishes)
Length maximum 82 cm (32¼in)

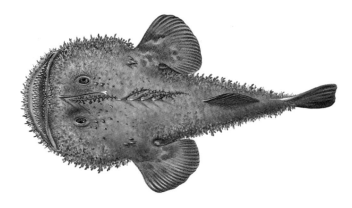

Identification Similar to the more common, larger species, with a massive broad head and wide mouth liberally armed with long, curved, sharp teeth. The first dorsal fin is a series of modified separate rays, the first of which has a flap of skin at its tip. Second dorsal fin normal in shape, with 8–9 fleshy rays. Three sharp spines on the side of the head just above and in front of the pectoral fins. A fleshy flap of skin above each eye. Coloration: variable, sandy brown to dark brown above with darker blotches. Ventrally pure white, but the lining of the body cavity is jet black and shows through the white skin.
Habitat A bottom-living fish which seems most abundant offshore at depths of 100–300m (55–164 fathoms). It lies at the surface of sandy or gravelly bottoms, having partly dug itself into the sea bed.
Breeding Spawns in autumn and winter, producing a gelatinous sheet of eggs which floats at the surface; the larvae and post-larvae are planktonic, with extremely long fin rays.
Food Any smaller fishes which can be enticed by the lure to the vicinity of its huge mouth.
Range From the western coasts of Scotland and Ireland southwards to the Canary Islands; throughout the Mediterranean.

Shore Clingfish
Lepadogaster lepadogaster

Family name Gobiesocidae (clingfishes)
Length maximum 6.5cm (2¼in)

Identification This is one of the larger clingfishes, which are distinguished by the well-developed sucker disc on the belly, the rather flattened head and anterior body, and single, low dorsal fin. This species has a prominent 'duck-billed' snout with thick lips, with a long, fringed tentacle on the posterior nostril. Both dorsal and anal fins long-based (16–19 rays in the former) and are joined to the tail fin. Coloration: variable, usually flesh-coloured, often reddish, with yellow-rimmed blue eye-spots on top of the head.
Habitat Most common between tide marks on shores with abundant boulders, and which are sheltered. These small fishes cling to the underside of stones, where they are protected from the waves.
Breeding Lays its golden eggs in a clump on the underside of a boulder, where they are guarded by a parent. The larvae and young fish planktonic at first but soon settle on the seabed.
Food No recorded information; probably eats crustaceans.
Range From western Scotland southwards to Morocco and throughout the western Mediterranean (where it is recognized as a subspecies).

Two-spotted Clingfish
Diplecogaster bimaculata

Family name Gobiesocidae (clingfishes)
Length maximum about 4cm (1½in)

Identification Head and body compressed from above; sucker disc on belly involving the pelvic fins. Head relatively small, with large eyes but short snout; lips thick and fleshy. Dorsal and anal fins placed well down the tail but short-based; dorsal with 5–7 rays only. Neither is joined to the tail fin. Coloration: variable, often bright red or pinkish with blue or brown spots; pale yellowish ventrally. Males have paired purple spots circled with yellow on the nape.
Habitat Lives in shallow water from mid-tide level on rocky shores down to a depth of about 55m (30 fathoms). Most abundant on rocks or stony ground, but occasionally found under large mollusc shells on sand or mud.
Breeding Spawns in spring and summer, the golden yellow eggs being laid in a patch under a stone or inside an empty shell. They are guarded by one of the adults. The larvae and young fish are pelagic but soon settle to a life on the sea bed.
Food Both adults and young eat small crustaceans, but no real study has been made of their diet.
Range From southern Norway and the Faroe Islands southwards to Gibraltar, and in the western basin of the Mediterranean.

Garfish
Belone belone

Family name Belonidae (garfishes)
Length maximum about 94cm (37in); usually up to 80cm (32in)
Weight maximum 1.4kg (3lb)

Identification The long, very slender body and elongate jaws forming a beak are distinctive. Both jaws have numerous small teeth in them. The dorsal and anal fins, set far back near the tail fin, have a high lobe in the anterior rays, the remainder lower. The lateral line runs from head to tail along the lower sides. Coloration: brilliant greeny-blue on the back and upper sides, the belly a gleaming silvery colour with golden tinges.
Habitat A surface-living fish of the open seas, which comes inshore into shallow water, particularly in summer. It lives mainly in the upper 20m (11 fathoms) of the sea, but can swim deeper. It forms large schools.
Breeding Spawns in coastal waters during May and June. The eggs have long, thin filaments on their surface, which tangle in algae, driftwood, floating fishing nets and other flotsam. When newly hatched the young have a long, thin body but short jaws. Later the lower jaw lengthens, but the upper jaw catches it up by the time the fish is about 9cm (3½in) long.
Food Eats small surface-living fishes, particularly young sandeels, herring and members of the cod family.
Range From northern Norway and southern Iceland southwards to Portugal. Close relatives live in the Mediterranean and the Black Sea.

Skipper
Scomberesox saurus

Family name Scomberesocidae (sauries)
Length maximum about 50cm (19½in)

Identification Similar to the garfish, being long and slender-bodied, with a long head and pointed, beak-like jaws which have rather small teeth. However, the body is flattened from side to side (not round as in the garfish), and seems rather higher. Dorsal and anal fins placed well down the tail, both similar in shape and both followed by a series of small finlets. Lateral line runs along the lower sides. Coloration: a beautiful clear green above, changing suddenly to bright silver with a yellowish tinge on the sides and belly.
Habitat A surface-living fish of the open ocean which travels in huge schools with the currents. These occasionally bring it into shallow coastal water in late autumn or early winter, otherwise it lives in the upper 20m (11 fathoms) of the ocean.
Breeding Lays its eggs in the open sea in summer. Short threads on the surface of the eggs allow them to tangle in floating algae or other flotsam.
Range Very widely distributed across the whole cold and temperate North Atlantic ocean. Also found in a broad band around the cool-temperate southern hemisphere. Occasionally swept into the North Sea by currents, but not resident there.

Flying Fish
Exocoetus volitans

Family name Exocoetidae (flying fishes)
Length maximum 18cm (7in)

Identification A typical flying fish, the body rounded in
cross-section but torpedo-shaped; head fairly short, snout
blunt. Dorsal and anal fin set far down the body, high in front,
lower posteriorly. Tail fin deeply forked, the lower lobe longer
than the upper. Pectoral fins enormous, reaching to the end of
the body; pelvic fins small (other flying fish species have long
pelvic fins). Coloration: brilliant blue above, silvery to white
below; fins mostly transparent.
Habitat Lives in the upper layers of the open ocean, probably
not found more than 5m (16ft) below the surface. Mostly seen
taking 'flight' out of the swell and skimming the surface before
re-entering the water, although it does rise at least 10m (32ft)
above the surface. These 'flights' are made escaping from
predators in the water below; in fact, the fish is actually gliding
as the wings do not flap.
Breeding Eggs are pelagic but lack the filaments that flying
fish eggs usually have. Unlike most of its relatives, the young
fish lacks barbels at the chin
Food No information available.
Range Worldwide in tropical and subtropical seas; has been
found in the Mediterranean. Other species occur (rarely) in
north European seas.

Sand-smelt
Atherina presbyter

Family name Atherinidae (sand-smelts or silversides)
Length maximum about 20cm (8in); usually about
15cm (6in)

Identification A rather slender-bodied fish, with a small
head but large eyes. Two dorsal fins, the first with 7–8 slender
rays, well separated from the second, which contains branched
rays. The anal fin is opposite the second dorsal and has two
thin spines and 13–16 branched rays. Tail fin slightly forked.
Body scales rather small but firmly attached. Coloration: back
and upper sides clear green with black specks on the edges of
the scales. An intense silvery line along the sides. Creamy
white ventrally.
Habitat A common fish in inshore waters, particularly in
estuaries, unpolluted harbours and saline lagoons. Most
abundant over sandy or muddy bottoms down to 20m
(11 fathoms). Young fish are often seen in intertidal pools
swimming in tightly organized schools.
Breeding Spawns in late spring and early summer. The eggs
have short filaments on their surface by which they are
attached to algae and other plants. Some spawning takes place
in large shore pools; elsewhere in coastal lagoons.
Food Not well known; eats small crustaceans and young fish.
Range From Denmark and Scotland (where rare) southwards
to Gibraltar and Morocco. Common in the southern North
Sea and the English Channel.

Opah
Lampris guttatus

Family name Lampridae (opahs)
Length maximum 1.5m (5ft)

Identification The body is deep and thickset; head moderate with a relatively small, but highly protrusible mouth, although it is toothless. Dorsal and anal fins long-based, the former with a high lobe. Tail fin lobes both high and shallowly forked; pelvic fins long and sickle-shaped; pectoral fins long and sickle-shaped and rigid on sides of body.

Habitat An open-ocean fish which lives probably 100–400m (55–219 fathoms) below the surface. It is a fast and powerful swimmer which usually avoids fishing nets; as a result it is known only from chance captures and a few strandings.

Breeding Nothing seems to be known.

Food Mostly squids but also fishes which occur in the area it inhabits (hake, blue whiting and other small members of the cod family).

Range In oceans across the world: from Norway to southern Africa, South America, Australia and north to Japan.

Deal-fish
Trachipterus trachypterus

Family name Trachipteridae (deal-fishes)
Length maximum about 2.5m (8ft 3in)

Identification Long, slender, deeply compressed body, so that while deep, it is also very narrow. The head is rather small, with a moderate eye and enormously protrusible mouth (when extended forms a tube). Dorsal fin very long-based, commencing above the head, running the length of the body. Tail fin developed only in the upper lobe, with long, well-separated rays. Pectoral fins small. Other fins absent. Coloration: body brilliant silver with broken dusky bars; fins deep red.
Habitat This is believed to be an inhabitant of the open ocean, living in the upper 914m (500 fathoms) of the water column. Probably comes nearer to the surface at night. Lifestyle virtually unknown as most specimens have been found drifting at the surface or stranded on the coast.
Breeding Nothing is known.
Food From the few observations that have been made, it appears to eat shrimps, squids and small fishes.
Range Widely distributed in the world's oceans, except for polar seas. In the North Atlantic from northern Norway southwards, but only off the open ocean coasts.

John Dory
Zeus faber

Family name
Zeidae (dories)
Length maximum
66cm (26in);
usually around
40cm (16in)
Weight
maximum
5.4kg (11lb 14oz)

Identification Quite unmistakable, with a deep body, massive head and large, highly protrusible jaws. The dorsal fin is composed of two sections – a series of long, strong spines joined to the second dorsal fin, which is of shorter, branched rays. Anal fin also double, with four strong spines separate from the more numerous branched rays in the second fin. Pelvic fin rays enormously long. A series of large spines on the body each side of the dorsal and anal fins. Coloration: dull yellowish-brown on the back, with lighter golden lines running across the back and sides; silvery-grey ventrally. Anal and pelvic fin membranes black. A conspicuous black eye-spot surrounded by a yellow ring on each side.

Habitat An inshore fish living in 1–5 m (5½–27 fathoms) of water. Usually solitary, sometimes in small schools. Often floats in the shadow of boats or driftwood, and among algae.

Breeding Mainly in late spring or summer, the eggs being small and pelagic, as are the larvae.

Food Eats a wide range of fishes which are stalked very slowly until close enough to be engulfed in the massive jaws.

Range Widely distributed from southern Norway and Scotland south to the Canary Islands and throughout the Mediterranean. Uncommon in northern parts of this range.

Boarfish
Capros aper

Family name Caproidae (boarfishes)
Length maximum 15cm (6in); usually about 10cm (4in)

Identification A deep-bodied, small fish with a large head, pointed snout and small but very protrusible jaws. The eyes are large. Dorsal fin in two sections, the first composed of strong, long spines separated from the second, which contains branched rays. The anal fin has similar, but short spines in front of the branched rays. Pelvic fins small, the anterior ray a heavy, strong spine with a rough anterior edge. Body scales very small but with toothed edges giving a rough sandpaper feel to the skin. Coloration: deep red with yellowish markings; in shallow water pale pink or straw coloured.
Habitat Probably common in areas of the lower continental shelf, particularly where the pink or yellow 'coral' grows. Occasionally caught in shallow water, especially off the western coasts of Europe following periods of upwelling when deep ocean currents wash the fish out of their usual habitat.
Breeding Spawns in summer; eggs and larvae are planktonic.
Food Eats only small crustaceans.
Range From southern Norway southwards to the Canary Islands and in the western Mediterranean. Mostly confined to coasts facing the open ocean; occasionally common in the western English Channel.

Three-spined Stickleback
Gasterosteus aculeatus

Family name Gasterosteidae (sticklebacks)
Length mostly about 5cm (2in); exceptionally up to 10cm (4in)

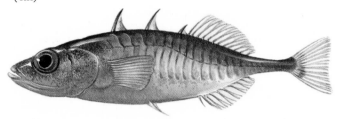

Identification A small fish with three sharp spines on the back, isolated from one another, the first two are strong and long, the third small. Dorsal and anal fins short, rather small and placed well down the back. Pelvic fins comprise a strong serrated spine on each side; pectoral fins broad and fan-like. Body naked or with a variable number of bony plates on the sides. Coloration: dark blue on the back, the sides and belly clear silver; males have red throats when breeding.
Habitat Well known as a freshwater fish, the stickleback lives also in estuarine conditions and in the northern parts of its range in the sea. Mostly found in rock pools with algae on the rocks, but some have been caught far out to sea living in the surface layers of the ocean.
Breeding Spawns in spring and summer. Mature males build a nest on the bottom out of algae and plant fibre in which the female lays her eggs. These are guarded by the male, who fans them to aerate the nest.
Food Virtually any small animals available, but mostly crustaceans and small fishes.
Range Coastal waters of the temperate northern hemisphere; in Europe from the White Sea to Portugal, including the coasts of the British Isles.

Fifteen-spined Stickleback

Spinachia spinachia

Family name Gasterosteidae (sticklebacks)
Length maximum 20cm (8in); usually around 15cm (6in)

Identification A very long, slender fish with a pointed snout
and a very long tail. The first dorsal fin is composed of a series
of 14–16 very short, isolated spines running along the back
from a level above the pectoral fins. These spines abut the
second dorsal fin, which is short but high; the anal fin is
similarly shaped but has only a single spine. The tail fin is
small and rounded. Body scaleless. Coloration: brown or
greenish-brown on the back and upper sides with darker bars;
yellowish ventrally. A brown blotch on the front of the dorsal
and anal fins.
Habitat A fish which is abundant in shallow inshore water in
depths from a few centimetres to 10m (15 fathoms). It is
occasionally found in estuaries, but is most abundant in tidal
pools in which there is fine green algae, or among eel grass and
algae on soft bottoms.
Breeding Spawns in spring and summer in a nest made by
the male of algae woven between stalks of seaweed and well
clear of the bottom. Up to 200 eggs are laid in the nest; they
are guarded by the male fish.
Food Almost entirely copepods, but a few other small
crustaceans and young fish are taken.
Range European seas from mid-Norway south to Biscay and
throughout the Baltic Sea.

Seahorse
Hippocampus ramulosus

Family name Syngnathidae (pipefishes and seahorses)
Length maximum 15cm (6in) from top of head to
unfurled tail

Identification Seahorses
have a very characteristic
shape, which means that they
are unmistakable as a group,
but the identification of the
species is difficult. In this
species the snout is long –
more than one-third of the
head length. The top of the
snout is straight, not concave.
Pectoral fins close behind the
head, with 15–18 rays in
each; dorsal fin 18–21 rays.
The junction between the end
of the abdomen and
beginning of the tail is
opposite the last third of the
dorsal fin. Anal fin very small,
tail fin absent. Coloration:
medium brown to dusky,
usually with small white
spots.

Habitat Seahorses are
usually most common in beds
of eel grass, turtle grass or
fine algae, to which they cling
by means of the curled tail.
However, they are capable of
swimming in the open sea and may voluntarily let go to
migrate. A substantial number are swept up on the coasts of
the English Channel and the Dutch North Sea. A summer
visitor in northern European seas.
Breeding The female produces eggs in summer, laid in a
pouch on the male's upper tail region. Inside the pouch they
hatch and grow until they are capable of swimming.
Food Small crustaceans, which are identified by eye and then
snapped up with a quick jerk of the snout.
Range Throughout the Mediterranean and the Black Sea,
northwards on the Atlantic coast as far west as Scotland.

Short-snouted Seahorse

Hippocampus hippocampus

Family name Syngnathidae (pipefishes and seahorses)
Length maximum 15cm (6in)

Identification In body shape a typical seahorse, but identification of species is difficult. The snout is short, its length at most one-third of the head length, usually less; dorsal profile of the snout concave. The eyes seem large by comparison and are about half the snout length. Dorsal fin with 16–18 rays; pectoral fin 13–15 rays. The level of the junction between the abdomen and the tail is in the first half of the dorsal fin. Anal fin minute; tail fin absent. Coloration: warm brown overall; inner side of the tail is pale.

Habitat Like other seahorses, this species hides among algae, eel grass and turtle grass in shallow water in southern European seas. Occasionally it is captured in the open sea, either when it has been washed out of its hiding place or when it is making a local migration. Much rarer than the other European seahorse.

Breeding In Mediterranean populations males carrying eggs in the brood pouch are caught April–October; newly born young are free-swimming in September and October.

Food Minute crustaceans selected by eye.

Range Throughout the Mediterranean; in the Atlantic between Madeira and Brittany. Northernmost record Guernsey.

Greater Pipefish
Syngnathus acus

Family name Syngnathidae (pipefishes and seahorses)
Length maximum about 47cm (18½in)

Identification This is one of the largest European pipefishes.
Its elongate, worm-like, but segmented body, and long, thin
snout are important features. It has a long-based dorsal fin
with 36–45 rays in it, moderately large pectoral fins and a
broad, fan-like tail; anal fin minute. The body is segmented
with rows of bony plates forming five rows on the abdomen
and four rows on the tail. The crown of the head is strongly
curved. Coloration: light brown, with darker markings on the
back and sides; creamy-brown on the belly and under the tail.
Habitat Lives in shallow water from 1m (39in) down to 20m
(11 fathoms). Mostly it is found in coastal waters over sand or
mud, but it is also common in estuaries. It does not seem to be
particularly associated with algae or eel grass, but is most often
caught in open water near the sea bed.
Breeding Males carrying eggs are most common in mid-
summer, June and July. The brood pouch is a double fold of
skin along each side of the tail, with an opening down the mid-
line. The tissue inside the pouch is thickened when the eggs
are within it.
Food Mostly small crustaceans and very young fish, which
are snapped up in the tubular mouth after being sighted.
Range From southern Norway and the Faroes, southwards to
the Canary Islands and throughout the Mediterranean.

Deep-snouted Pipefish
Syngnathus typhle

Family name Syngnathidae (pipefishes and seahorses)
Length maximum about 30cm (12in)

Identification Long, slender body, with the typical
segmented appearance of this group of pipefishes, with five
rows of bony plates in line along the body and four rows on
the tail. The main identifying features are the deep snout,
which is laterally compressed, and the upturned mouth with
protruding lower jaw. The dorsal fin is long, with 28–41 rays;
pectoral fins are small, but the tail fin is moderate in size. Anal
fin minute. There are 16–18 body rings and 33–38 tail rings.
Coloration: light greeny-brown above, sometimes plain brown;
ventrally paler.
Habitat Lives in eel-grass beds on sandy bottoms and among
algae on rocky shores. A coastal water fish, it is found at
depths of 4–20m (2–11 fathoms). Frequently found in
estuarine conditions and common in the Baltic Sea.
Breeding Males carry the eggs in their pouch June–August.
Incubation may last for four weeks, but depends on
temperature. The brood pouch is a double flap of skin along
the front of the tail with an opening in the mid-line.
Food Eats small crustaceans, particularly copepods.
Range From mid-Norway and the southern Baltic,
southwards to Gibraltar, and thence through the
Mediterranean and the Black Sea.

Straight-nosed Pipefish
Nerophis ophidion

Family name Syngnathidae (pipefishes and seahorses)
Length maximum 30cm (12in) females; 25cm (10in) males

Identification Very long and slender, the body is rounded in cross-section and the segments of body and tail noticeable only as rings without angles on the body or the tail. The snout is straight and moderately long, tapering to a small mouth. The dorsal fin is long-based but low, with short rays, 33–34 rays in the fin. Pectoral, anal and tail fins absent. The body is very long with 28–32 body rings, much longer than the tail fin. Coloration: greeny-brown on the back, light green on the sides; females have pale blue lines along the body.

Habitat A shallow-water pipefish found on most coasts in water 5–25m (3–14 fathoms), sometimes shallower. It is strongly associated with eel-grass beds in shallow water on sand and mud, but is also common in rocky areas, where it lives among long-stranded seaweeds. It is often common in estuaries and also in the low-salinity Baltic Sea.

Breeding Males are found carrying eggs mostly May–August. They have no egg pouch, for the eggs merely adhere to the concave belly. The young hatch and are free-swimming at a length of about 9mm (¾in).

Food All ages eat crustaceans and their larvae.

Range From mid-Norway and the Scottish coast southwards to Gibraltar and throughout the Mediterranean, the Black Sea and the Baltic.

Worm Pipefish
Nerophis lumbriciformis

Family name Syngnathidae (pipefishes and seahorses)
Length maximum 15cm (6in)

Identification A small, almost worm-like pipefish, with the body round in cross-section. The body and tail are segmented but there are no bony plates on the skin, nor is it angled where the plates meet. The snout is very short and blunt, strongly concave on its upper surface. Dorsal fin long-based, with 24–28 rays, but low in outline; pectoral, anal and tail fins absent. Coloration: dark green, brown or almost black on the back and sides, matching the colour of the algae in which it lives, with lighter, almost white mottling under the throat.
Habitat This small pipefish is relatively common on the shore and in shallow water in rocky areas. It is, however, confined to areas where there is a strong growth of seaweeds with thin, rounded stems. The pipefish hides in the algae, mimicking its colour and appearing to be yet another stem of weed. It also hides under stones and seaweed on the shore.
Breeding Males carry the eggs in a shallow groove under the belly June–August. The young hatch at a length of about 1cm ($\frac{2}{3}$in) and at first live in the plankton.
Food Small crustaceans and their larvae.
Range From southern Norway, Orkney and the west coast of the British Isles, southwards to Gibraltar.

Snake Pipefish
Entelurus aequoreus

Family name Syngnathidae (pipefishes and seahorses)
Length 60cm (24in) females

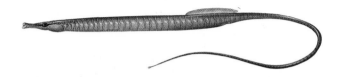

Identification Largest of the European pipefishes. Body and
tail very long and slender, with the surface smooth and
rounded in cross-section. There is almost no sign of the bony
rings which are a feature of other pipefishes. The head is long,
with a long, concave snout and a tiny mouth. Dorsal fin rays
short, but the fin is long-based. A minute tail fin with very
short rays; no pectoral or anal fins. Dorsal fin with 37–47 rays,
mostly on the trunk in front of the level of the vent.
Coloration: pale brown or yellowish-olive, each body ring
picked out in pale blue at the edges.
Habitat One of the few pipefishes which lives in the open sea,
and in deeper water than other species. It is most common at
10–100m (5½–55 fathoms) among kelp and other deep-water
seaweeds, but large and young specimens are caught at or near
the surface far offshore and are more or less oceanic.
Breeding Males carry the eggs in a shallow groove on the
belly in mid-summer. The young are about 12mm (½in) on
hatching and live near the surface.
Food No data available; probably eats small crustaceans.
Range From southern Iceland and mid-Norway southwards
to Gibraltar and the Azores.

Black Scorpionfish
Scorpaena porcus

Family name Scorpaenidae (scorpionfishes)
Length maximum 30cm (12in); usually around 15cm (6in)

Identification A stout-bodied fish with a broad, spiny head; two spines just above the upper jaw on the snout, ridge beneath the eye with 2–3 spines and several on the nape and the preoperculum. A deep depression on top of the head. Eyes large, diameter greater than snout length. Large branched tentacle above each eye, as long as the eye diameter. Dorsal fin with 12 strong spines and nine branched rays; anal fin with three strong spines and 5–6 branched rays, pectoral fin with broad with 16–18 rays. Coloration: brownish or reddish-brown with darker spots and bands; three vertical dark bands on the tail; a dark patch on the spiny dorsal fin between spines eight and nine; lighter ventrally. **Note** The dorsal spines are equipped with venom glands, so handle this fish carefully.
Habitat Lives among rocks from the shoreline down to 50m (27 fathoms), usually among algae or plants. Its basic coloration varies according to the background on which it lives and it is almost impossible to locate under water. If disturbed, it darts away at high speed, then settles again.
Breeding Said to breed in late summer and autumn. The eggs form a nearly transparent clump, laid in crevices. Very little information available on its life history.
Food Eats small fishes, especially blennies, gobies and wrasses, which approach its vicinity. Feeds mostly at night.
Range From the Biscay coast of France southwards to the Canary Islands, westwards to the Azores, and throughout the Mediterranean.

Tub Gurnard
Trigla lucerna

Family name Triglidae (gurnards)
Length maximum 75cm (30in); usually around 60cm (24in)
Weight maximum 5.5kg (12lb 3oz)

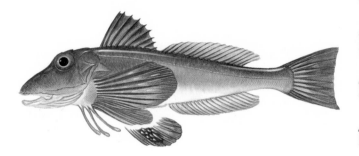

Identification A very large, heavy-headed gurnard. The snout has two slight lobes on either side, each bearing small spines at the tips; the snout is pointed in profile. The eyes are relatively small, the diameter about 1.5 times into the depth of the cheek. Two dorsal fins, the first high and spiny, the second low and with branched rays only; anal fin of similar size and shape. Pectoral fins with the lower three rays separate and finger-like; remainder of the fin very long, reaching well past the anal fin origin. Scales small, not enlarged or spiny on the lateral line. Coloration: back and sides deep reddish-brown to rose red, underside pinkish; pectoral fins brilliant peacock blue, green-spotted and red on edge.
Habitat Common in inshore waters of 20–150m (11–82 fathoms) on mud and muddy-sand bottoms. Young ones live closer inshore than this. It is mainly a bottom-living fish, although it can be caught in mid-water. Gurnards make loud grunting noises using special muscles attached to the large swim-bladder; these help the schools keep together.
Breeding Spawns in summer; details of spawning place are rather scanty.
Food Bottom-living organisms, chiefly crabs, shrimps and other crustaceans, including some fishes. These are detected in the sand by the feeler-like pectoral rays.
Range From mid-Norway and Scottish waters, southwards to the Canary Islands, throughout the Mediterranean.

Red Gurnard

Aspitrigla cuculus

Family name Triglidae (gurnards)
Length 40cm (16in)

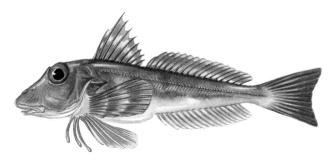

Identification The red gurnard seems rather stout-bodied compared with the tub. The head is moderately large, with three short spines each side; it is pointed in profile but not acutely so, and is concave. The first dorsal fin is spiny and high; the second fin is long-based, low and the same shape as the anal. Pectoral fin large, but extends only to the beginning of the anal fin; the first rays are long, separate and finger-like. Body scales small, but lateral line is covered by large, flattened scales with a weak point. Coloration: deep red overall; ventrally pinkish. Pectoral fins red above with a darker edge.

Habitat A bottom-living fish found in shallow water 20–100m (11–55 fathoms), usually on sandy or gravel bottoms, but occasionally on mud or rough ground. Gurnards explore the sea bed with the finger-like rays of the lower pectoral fins and raise their head ends above the level of the sea bed on these 'stilts'.

Breeding Spawns in summer; details are little known.

Food Eats mostly crustaceans, particularly shrimps and crabs, but also other bottom-living invertebrates and fishes.

Range From southern Scottish waters to the English Channel, southwards to Morocco and in the western Mediterranean. Found only in the southern North Sea.

Grey Gurnard
Eutrigla gurnardus

Family name Triglidae (gurnards)
Length maximum 45cm (18in); usually around 30cm (12in)
Weight maximum 1.1kg (2lb 7oz)

Identification A slender-bodied gurnard with a sharply
pointed snout. The snout and 'forehead' are straight in
outline. The eyes are large, their diameter as large as the depth
of the cheek. The first dorsal fin short-based, high, with long
spines, the second with branched rays, long-based, about the
same length as the anal fin. Pectoral fin moderate in size but
not reaching the origin of the anal fin. Scales small and
embedded, the lateral line with sharp spines, and the back
(either side of the dorsal fins) with large spines. Coloration:
back and sides brownish-grey with small, creamy spots;
ventrally dull white. A dusky patch on the end of the first
dorsal fin.
Habitat A common gurnard living on sandy bottoms, but
also found on mud in shell-covered grounds. It is most
common at depths of 20–50m (11–27 fathoms), but small
specimens are caught in much shallower water. It is mostly a
bottom-living fish, but is occasionally caught in mid-water.
Breeding Spawns April–August in moderately deep water.
Mature between two and three years of age.
Food Bottom-living invertebrates and fishes, such as shrimps
and small crabs, gobies, sandeels and small flatfishes.
Range From southern Iceland and mid-Norway southwards
to Morocco; throughout the Mediterranean and Black Sea.
Very common in the North Sea.

Streaked Gurnard

Trigloporus lastoviza

Family name Triglidae (gurnards)
Length maximum 40cm (16in); usually to 36cm (14in)
Weight maximum 600g (1lb 6oz)

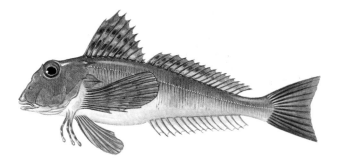

Identification A thickset, heavy-bodied gurnard with a blunt
snout and near vertical profile. The first dorsal fin is high,
moderately long-based, with about 10 strong spines; the
second dorsal fin is lower, composed of branched rays and
about the same length as the anal fin. Pectoral fins moderately
large, extending to beyond the origin of the anal fin. The body
is covered by distinct vertical ridges of skin which originate at
the lateral line; the lateral line scales have small spines; a line
of larger scales either side of the dorsal fin bases. Coloration:
dull red, even reddish-brown above, with darker patches. The
pectoral fins are greyish, tinged with red, and with rows of
blue spots.
Habitat A bottom-living gurnard which is found in
moderately deep water of 40–100m (22–55 fathoms). It lives
mostly on sandy and muddy grounds offshore, especially
occurring between rocky patches. Relatively uncommon north
of the English Channel, although it occurs fairly regularly in
the Irish Sea and North Sea. It probably migrates northwards
in summer.
Breeding Spawns in deep water in summer; little is recorded
of its breeding biology.
Food Almost exclusively crustaceans, especially swimming
crabs.
Range From the coast of western Scotland southwards to the
Canary Islands, and throughout the Mediterranean.

Bull-trout

Myoxocephalus scorpius

Family name Cottidae (sculpins)
Length maximum 30cm (12in); twice this size in Arctic seas
Weight maximum 1.1kg (2lb 7oz)

Identification A large sculpin, with an enormous broad head, rather flattened from top to bottom. Several small spines on top of head, two short, stout spines on the preoperculum and a weak, flattened spine on the gill cover itself. Two dorsal fins, the first a little shorter-based than the second but composed of strong spines; anal fin small, as are pelvics (three rays only). Pectoral fin, enormously broad, runs forward ventrally to the throat. A patch of roughened skin either side of the anterior lateral line is composed of small spines. The gill membrane forms a flap under the throat. Coloration: greeny-brown above, blotched with dark patches; ventrally cherry red to orange with rounded white spots.
Habitat Widespread along north European coasts, found mainly at 4–60m (2–33 fathoms). In the Arctic region it is found between tidemarks; elsewhere it is found just below low tide. It is particularly common on muddy and sandy bottoms.
Breeding Spawns December–March, the eggs being laid between rocks in a clump protected by the male. They hatch in 5–12 weeks depending on temperature (the colder it is, the longer they take).
Food A wide range of bottom-living fishes and crustaceans.
Range From Spitzbergen and Iceland southwards to the English Channel.

Sea Scorpion
Taurulus bubalis

Family name Cottidae (sculpins)
Length maximum to 18cm (7in)
Weight maximum 225g (8oz)

Identification A thickset, relatively slender body, which is, however, deep; the head is enormously broad. There are small, low spines on the back of the head and a short, flat spine on the operculum; the preoperculum has a very long, sharp spine which points upwards and back. Two dorsal fins, the first rounded and rather low, shorter based than the second dorsal fin. Pectoral fins large, fan-like, extending almost under the throat. The membrane running from the gill covers joins the sides of the throat and does not form a flap crossing the throat. A small, fleshy flap at the angle of the upper jaw. Coloration: usually greeny-brown, sometimes reddish, always heavily blotched; yellowish ventrally.
Habitat A common fish on rocky shores and just below tide-marks. Always found hiding under algae. Has been caught down to 30m (16 fathoms); most common on shore, but these are often small, young fish.
Breeding Lays its eggs in clumps among algae on the shore in early spring. The eggs are guarded by an adult. After hatching they swim in mid-water offshore, but quickly return to the coast.
Food Eats a wide range of crustaceans and small fishes.
Range From northern Norway and Iceland, southwards to northern Spain; uncommon south of Brittany.

Hooknose
Agonus cataphractus

Family name Agonidae (poachers)
Length maximum 20cm (8in); usually only to 15cm (6in)

Identification Immediately identifiable because the head and body are encased in hard, bony plates, those on the body with joints so that the fish can move. A strong, curved spine on the lower side of each gill cover, and a double curved spine on the tip of the snout. Many short barbels on the underside of the head. Two dorsal fins, the first with flexible spines forming a short fin, the second a little longer based (similar to the anal fin in shape). Tail slender with a small fin at the tip. Coloration: dull brown on the back with four darker saddles; ventrally creamy white.
Habitat A common fish on soft bottoms of mud or sand in depths of 20–270m (11–148 fathoms) but which is also found in 2m (6ft 6in) of water. It lives close to the sea bed.
Breeding Spawns February–May, the female laying clumps of eggs between the basal branches of kelp and other seaweeds. The eggs take a long time to hatch. Very little is known about the biology of this species.
Food Eats small crustaceans, brittlestars, worms and small molluscs; its diet is very unspecialized.
Range From the White Sea, northern Norway and Iceland south to the English Channel, where it is uncommon.

Lumpsucker

Cyclopterus lumpus

Family name Cyclopteridae (lumpsuckers and sea-snails)
Length maximum 60cm (24in); usually 30–40cm (12–16in)
Weight maximum 9.3kg (20lb 9oz)

Identification A highly distinctive fish, with a large, almost spherical body with row of large, rough-spined bony plates on the back, sides and belly. The fins are small; dorsal and anal fins similar in size and shape and closely set to the tail fin. Pectoral fin rather small, long-based and running under the throat. A large and powerful sucker disc on the belly. In young fish the first dorsal fin forms a high, blunt crest, but it is largely obscured in the adult. Coloration: very variable, from greenish to brown on the back, paler ventrally. Males have orange-red tints on the belly in the breeding season.
Habitat Primarily a bottom-living species which is found on and among rocks on the seashore, while the young fish live among seaweed. At all ages they cling by means of the sucker disc. Despite this, numerous large specimens are caught in mid-water, so they are obviously capable of pelagic life also.
Breeding Spawns on the shore and inshore on rocky coasts. The eggs are laid in large clumps February–May; they are guarded by the male.
Food Small fishes, crustaceans and polychaete worms.
Range North Atlantic, from northern Norway and the White Sea, west Greenland, southwards to the English Channel and to the Gulf of Maine, USA.

Sea-snail
Liparis liparis

Family name Cyclopteridae (lumpsuckers and sea-snails)
Length maximum 18cm (7in); usually around 10cm (4in)

Identification A strange, jelly-like fish with a small, rounded body, tadpole-like in shape, with a broad head. A long-based dorsal fin with 33–35 rays, embedded in jelly-like skin; a little longer than the anal fin. Pectoral fin broad and running under the throat as a fringe. Skin of body loose and flabby. A large sucker disc on the belly. Coloration: very variable; usually dull brown above, often patterned; lighter below.
Habitat A fairly common fish in inshore seas at 5–150m (3–82 fathoms). Most abundant on mud or muddy sand. It is not found between tide marks.
Breeding Spawns in winter, January–March, its eggs being laid on the bottom in small, walnut-sized clumps. Usually they are laid in short algae or among hydroids. The eggs hatch in 6–8 weeks and shortly after hatching are pelagic.
Food Eats mainly crustaceans, also worms and small fishes.
Range Arctic coasts of northern Russia to northern Norway, Iceland and Greenland, south to the British Isles and the Gulf of Maine, USA.

Flying Gurnard
Dactylopterus volitans

Family name Dactylopteridae (flying gurnards)
Length maximum 55cm (22in)

Identification This is a quite unmistakable fish. The body is relatively long but rounded in cross-section, the head large, blunt and heavily armoured, with the hard bone extending on to the back, and a massive spine from the lower part of the gill cover reaching beyond the level of the pelvic fins. Pectoral fins enormous and brightly coloured, frequently expanded laterally. Two dorsal fins, the first wholly spiny and with two separate spines in front of the fin; the second fin with flexible rays; anal fin a similar shape to the second dorsal. Body covered with hard scales which form ridges along the sides of the tail fin. Coloration: brown on the back with irregular lighter patches; sometimes reddish with lighter spots and flecks. The upper side of the pectoral fins is brownish with creamy spots, brilliant spots of blue towards the edge and a blue band on the edge itself.
Habitat Lives on sandy and muddy bottoms, usually at 10–30m (5½–16½ fathoms) and rarely down to 80m (44 fathoms). Explores the sea bed with the shorter front rays of the pectoral fins. This fish does not fly; under water it spreads its huge pectoral fins and swims with them spread, but mostly they are displayed suddenly to startle potential predators.
Breeding No real information.
Food Bottom-living organisms, mostly crustaceans.
Range Western English Channel southwards to Morocco and throughout the Mediterranean.

Bass
Dicentrarchus labrax

Family name Percichthyidae (sea basses)
Length maximum 1m (39in); usually around 60cm (24in)
Weight maximum 8.6kg (19lb)

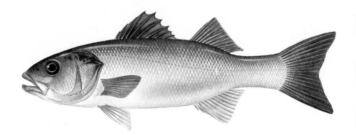

Identification A slim, torpedo-shaped body with a relatively large head; wide mouth but fairly small eyes. Two dorsal fins, the first with 8–9 strong but slender spines, well separated from the second, which is shorter and has mostly branched rays. Anal fin similar in shape to second dorsal but with three short spines in front. Body covered with large scales. A row of forward-pointing spines on the lower edge of each preoperculum; flat, weak spines on the gill cover. Coloration: greeny-grey on the back, shading into brilliantly silver sides and silvery-white on the belly. A dusky patch on the gill covers.
Habitat An actively swimming schooling fish which is particularly common in coastal waters in warm seasons, although it also occurs close to offshore reefs and in estuaries. It is seasonally migratory, moving northwards and into inshore waters in summer. It lives near the surface and is particularly found where the water is disturbed (e.g. near breakers and on rock faces).
Breeding March–June, mostly in inshore waters. The young are pelagic but quickly enter estuaries, where they stay for a year or two.
Food Eats a wide range of fishes, particularly herring and sprat, and sandeels. Also eats crustaceans.
Range From Scotland and Denmark southwards to Morocco; throughout the Mediterranean.

Wreckfish
Polyprion americanus

Family name Perchthyidae (sea basses)
Length maximum 2m (6ft 6in)
Weight maximum 4.8kg (10lb 10oz)

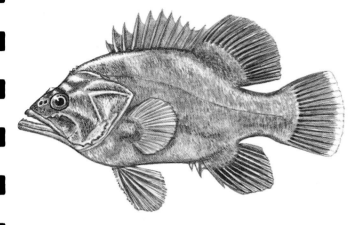

Identification A large, heavy-bodied fish with a massive head
and protruding lower jaw. The dorsal fins are continuous; the
first has 11 strong spines, the last of which is joined to the
second dorsal fin with 12 branched rays. Anal fin short-based
with three strong spines. Tail fin broad and square-cut. Body
scales are small, firmly attached and with rough edges; the
scales run up the bases of the dorsal and anal fins. The mouth
is large, as are the eyes; the preoperculum is spiny on the edge
and the operculum has a strong bony strut running across it,
ending in a spine. Coloration: back and sides dark brown,
shading to yellowish on the belly; large darker blotches on
back and sides.
Habitat An open-sea fish, which in northern waters is most
often seen floating beside drifting wreckage and large flotsam
near the surface. Elsewhere it lives close to the sea bed in
depths of 100–200m (55–109 fathoms).
Breeding Spawns in summer; very little information
available.
Food Eats mostly fishes, but also crustaceans and squids.
Range In the Atlantic from Norway southwards to West
Africa, throughout the Mediterranean and off North America;
also found in the temperate southern Atlantic.

Comber
Serranus cabrilla

Family name Serranidae (sea perches)
Length maximum around 30cm (12in)
Weight maximum 880g (1lb 13oz)

Identification A moderately stout-bodied fish with a rather
large head. Two dorsal fins, the first with 11 slender spines,
joined to the second which has only branched rays. Anal fin
with three spines and 7–8 branched rays. The lower jaw is
prominent and the mouth large; eyes moderately large. The
preoperculum edge has fine teeth; three flat spines on each gill
cover. Coloration: back and upper sides brown with 7–9
darker vertical stripes (almost chocolate coloured); head with
rows of pale blue or greenish stripes on the lower side and
running on to the belly.
Habitat Lives near the sea bed in coastal waters from
20–55m (11–20 fathoms) and reputedly deeper. It lives on a
wide range of substrate, mud or sand with occasional
boulders, and among turtle-grass beds. Probably most
common on rocky bottoms. Uncommon in British waters.
Breeding Breeds July–August in the English Channel. There
are few details of its breeding biology, but it is known to be
hermaphrodite.
Food Eats a wide range of fishes, crustaceans and also squids.
Range From the western English Channel southwards to
Madeira and the Canary Islands, and throughout the
Mediterranean.

Dusky Perch

Epinephelus marginatus

Family name Serranidae (sea perches)
Length maximum 1.4m (55in); usually around 1m (39in)
Weight maximum 12.7kg (28lb)

Identification This is the largest European sea perch, and has a relatively robust body and large head. The dorsal fins are continuous, the first with 11 strong spines joining the second which has 13–16 branched rays. Anal fin with three strong spines and 8–9 rays. The head is large and broad with a wide mouth. Fine serrations along the edge of the preoperculum and three flat spines on the end of the operculum. Coloration: deep brown with irregular lighter blotches on the sides; yellowish-brown under the belly; dorsal fin with an orange or pink edge, other fins with a cream edge.
Habitat Typically haunts rocky bottoms, over and between the rocks, but large specimens live in caves (where these exist). It is usually solitary. Found at depths of 8–20m (4½–109 fathoms), but most abundant at 50m (27 fathoms). Occasional specimens wander northwards into north European seas.
Breeding Spawns during summer in the Mediterranean. Probably does not breed in northern waters.
Food Eats octopuses and occasionally squids, but will also eat a wide range of fish.
Range From southern England and Ireland southwards to the West African coast and throughout the Mediterranean. Large, probably very old specimens have been heavily overfished by divers in the Mediterranean.

Painted Comber
Serranus scriba

Family name Serranidae (sea perches)
Length maximum about 36cm (14in); usually around 25cm (10in)

Identification Slightly stouter than the comber and with a relatively large head. Two dorsal fins, the first with 10 strong spines joined to the second, which has 14–16 branched rays; anal fin shorter based, with three spines and 7–8 branched rays. Tail fin moderate in size, smoothly rounded in outline. Preoperculum with fine serrations on the rear edge; three large flat spines on the gill cover. Body scales small, about 65–75 in the lateral line. Coloration: very distinctive; back reddish-brown to purple, 5–7 vertical dark brown bars on the sides; a diffuse pale blue patch on the lower sides; narrow, wriggling blue lines and red blotches on the head.
Habitat An inshore species which lives mostly over rocks and turtle-grass beds from 2–150m (6½–82 fathoms). Usually solitary; does not appear to move far from its home territory.
Breeding Like others of this group, is hermaphrodite. It breeds in summer (April–August) in the Mediterranean. Breeding habits outside the Mediterranean unknown.
Food Eats mainly fishes but also some crustaceans and squids.
Range From the coast of Brittany southwards to Morocco and the Canary Islands; throughout the Mediterranean.

Brown Comber

Serranus hepatus

Family name Serranidae (sea perches)
Length maximum 14cm (5½in)

Identification Similar in general shape to its relatives but the body is distinctly deeper; the head is also deeper and appears large, while the snout and forehead are strongly curved. Mouth and eyes large; the diameter of the eyes as great as the snout length. Two dorsal fins, the first composed of 10 long slender spines continuous with the second dorsal, which has 11–13 branched rays. Anal fin with three spines and 6–7 branched rays. Head scaly posteriorly, with serrations on the edge of the preoperculum and three flat spines on the gill cover. Scales on body moderate in size, 44–50 in the lateral line. Coloration: dull brown with 2–5 darker vertical bars across the sides, the third bar branched at the dorsal end. Characteristic black spot at the junction of the dorsal fins. Yellow lines on head.

Habitat Lives on sandy and muddy bottoms and in turtle-grass beds at depths of 5–100m (2¾–55 fathoms). It is also found on rocks. Tends to be solitary.

Breeding Breeds in summer (April–August). Like several of its relatives, it is hermaphrodite.

Food Eats small fishes, squids, small octopuses and crustaceans.

Range Distributed from northern Portugal southwards to the Canary Islands and throughout the Mediterranean.

Scad
Trachurus trachurus

Family name Carangidae (jacks, scad, horse mackerels)
Length maximum about 50cm (19½in); usually about
25cm (10in)
Weight maximum 1.5kg (3lb 5oz)

Identification More or less slender-bodied with a large head.
Two dorsal fins, the first with seven slender spines (the last
one being very short) just separate from the much longer
second dorsal fin. Anal fin also long-based, similar in size, with
two separate short spines in front of the fin. A very distinctive
feature is the series of bony scutes which runs from head to
tail, each with a small spine, which grows harder and larger
towards the tail. Coloration: dark blue with greenish tints, the
sides silvery flushed with gold; white ventrally; a dusky spot on
the edge of the gill cover.
Habitat A pelagic schooling fish which frequently occurs in
great abundance. Often caught in inshore waters near the
surface, most are captured in schools just off the sea bed in
100m (55 fathoms) of water. Young fish in their first year are
frequently seen swimming close to jellyfishes.
Breeding Spawning takes place mostly in spring and
summer, later further north. The eggs and larvae are pelagic,
as are the young fish (but see above).
Food Mostly crustaceans, squids and small fishes.
Range From southern Norway and Scottish waters
southwards to the Moroccan coast and throughout the
Mediterranean. A subspecies replaces this form along the West
African coast.

Shark Sucker
Remora remora

Family name Echeneidae (shark suckers, remoras)
Length maximum 45cm (18in); rarely more than 15cm (6in)

Identification Instantly identifiable in the seas of northern
Europe as only the one species occurs there. This is the only
fish to have a sucker disc on top of the head; it looks like a
venetian blind with a central bar. Disc has 17–19 pairs of slats,
and its posterior edge does not extend past the pelvic fin tips.
The disc with its slats is a modified first dorsal fin. The second
dorsal is low, composed of branched rays and shorter based
than the anal fin. The head is relatively small with a very
protuberant lower jaw. Coloration: dark greyish-brown above
and below; the pectoral fin tips light.
Habitat An oceanic species which accompanies the blue
shark (and possibly other migratory sharks) to northern
European waters as they migrate. Frequently they are seen
attached by the sucker to the underside of the shark but they
also swim in close formation with it. Occasionally they keep
station on turtles and even slow-moving ships.
Breeding No data; does not breed in northern seas.
Food Mostly parasitic copepods attached to the host sharks'
skin and gills. It may also pick up small planktonic crustaceans
near the host.
Range In Europe from western Ireland down to Madeira and
in the western Mediterranean. Strongly associated with the
host's seasonal migrations.

Dolphin-fish
Coryphaena hippurus

Family name Coryphaenidae (dolphin fishes)
Length maximum 2m (6ft 6in); common to 1m (39in)

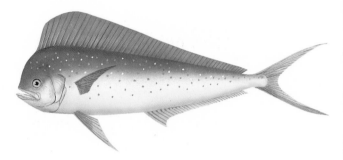

Identification A long, slender-bodied fish compressed from side to side. Head small, eyes moderately large; profile of head steep, continuing to the origin of the dorsal fin. Dorsal fin long-based, running from above head to tail fin; anal fin about half the length of dorsal but similar in shape; tail fin forked. Coloration: brilliant metallic blue-green; yellowish ventrally. This striking colour fades quickly after death.
Habitat An open-sea, tropical species which is rarely found as far north as Biscay. Forms schools in the upper 100m (55 fathoms) of water. Small specimens frequently accompany floating objects and ships, often in their shadow.
Breeding Spawns in the warm season; eggs and larvae pelagic. Growth is very rapid.
Food Occasionally eats squids and crustaceans, but feeds almost entirely on surface-living fishes. Flying fishes are an important item, and the presence of dolphin-fishes is usually the cause of their leaving the water.
Range Worldwide in tropical and subtropical seas. In Europe southwards from Spain and throughout the Mediterranean (where common). Rarely extends as far north as Biscay.

Black Sea-bream

Spondyliosoma cantharus

Family name Sparidae (sea-breams)
Length maximum 51cm (20in); mostly around 35cm (14in)
Weight maximum 3.1kg (6lb 14oz)

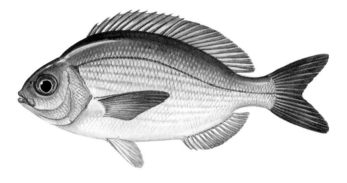

Identification A moderately deep-bodied sea-bream with a small head, rounded profile and jaws which reach to the level of the eye at most. A single dorsal fin, the first half of which has 11 sharp spines, and the second half branched rays. Teeth are sharply pointed, slightly curved and relatively small; they are slightly larger in the front of the jaws but are similar in shape in front and sides. Coloration: back greyish, sides silvery-grey with six or seven dusky vertical bars; fins grey, edge of tail dusky.

Habitat Lives just above the sea bed in water down to 100m (55 fathoms) but often taken in 10m (5½ fathoms). It forms schools close to reefs and wrecks, usually just above and to one side of them. In northern European waters it seems to be migratory as it becomes distinctly more abundant in summer.

Breeding Makes a nest on the sea bed, usually in a sandy area, the male excavating a shallow hollow. The eggs are guarded by the male (which has much brighter coloration at this time), and the young fish form a loose school close to the nest after hatching. Spawning takes place in April and May.

Food Mostly bottom-living invertebrates, particularly those encrusted on rocks, and small crustaceans.

Range From mid-Norway and Scotland (where uncommon) southwards to Angola; throughout the Mediterranean.

Red Sea-bream
Pagellus bogaraveo

Family name Sparidae (sea-breams)
Length maximum 51cm (20in); usually around 35cm (14in)
Weight maximum 4.3kg (9lb 8oz)

Identification Moderately deep-bodied, with a rounded snout and large eyes, their diameter greater than the snout length and also the cheek depth. Teeth small, sharp and curved, but not massive; in the sides of the jaws two or three rows of rounded, flattened teeth. Dorsal fin long, with 12 spines in the front, the rear part with 12–13 branched rays; anal fin shorter with three spines and 12–13 branched rays. Pectoral fins long and pointed. Coloration: reddish on the back and upper sides, silvery with a rose tinge on the sides; rounded, dusky blotch between the base of the pectoral fin and the origin of the first dorsal fin.

Habitat Probably the most abundant sea-bream in northern European waters but nowhere common. It lives in moderate depths of 50–100m (27–55 fathoms) as a small fish, but the largest specimens occur in 150–300m (81–162 fathoms). Young fish in particular form large schools, but the adults are usually found in small groups. They tend to be most common close to wrecks and reefs.

Breeding Spawns in late summer to autumn in deep water. The eggs are pelagic but the young fish drift towards shore.

Food Mainly fish, but large specimens eat a range of deep-water shrimps and crabs, and occasionally squids.

Range From southern Norway southwards to the Canary Islands; throughout the Mediterranean

Gilthead

Sparus aurata

Family name Sparidae (sea-breams)
Length maximum 70cm (28in); usually 30–35cm (12–14in)
Weight maximum 4.5kg (9lb 15oz)

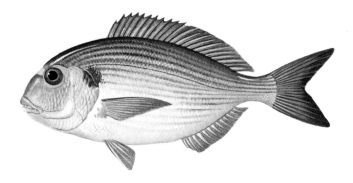

Identification Deep-bodied with a relatively large, deep head
and small eyes set well up on the sides of it; the eye diameter is
less than the length of the snout. Cheeks deep and scaled,
preoperculum scaleless, but gill covers with scales. Dorsal fin
long and in two sections, the anterior part with 11 strong
spines, the second part with 13–14 branched rays. Anal fin
relatively short, with three strong spines followed by 11–12
branched rays. Teeth in jaws large and strong, 4–6 strong
pointed teeth in front and 2–4 rows of bluntly rounded teeth
in the sides. Coloration: back grey-blue, sides silvery, a large
dusky blotch behind the eye, scarlet on the edge of the gill
cover, golden stripe over the forehead between the eyes.
Habitat A shallow-water sea-bream living on sandy bottoms
and in turtle-grass beds; it is particularly attracted to estuaries
and low-salinity lagoons. It is usually solitary or found in small
schools, particularly when young.
Breeding Spawns October–December. Hermaphrodite, it is
male in the early years of its life and female later. Does not
spawn north of Biscay.
Food Eats large quantities of molluscs, especially mussels and
crustaceans, and fishes.
Range From southern England and Ireland southwards to
the Canary Islands and throughout the Mediterranean.

Dentex
Dentex dentex

Family name Sparidae (sea-breams)
Length maximum 1m (39in); usually 35–50cm (14–20in)

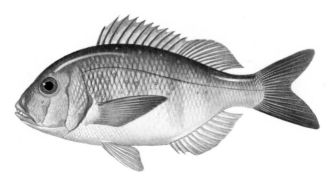

Identification Body oval, profile of head and anterior back strongly curved, but straight in young. Old males have a conspicuous bump on the forehead. Eyes relatively large and snout long. Two dorsal fins, the first with rather large, sharp spines, joined to the second fin, which has branched rays. The first dorsal has 11 spines, the second 11–12 rays. Jaws with sharply pointed teeth in their sides but with 4–6 long, strong canines in the front. Lateral line with 62–68 scales.
Coloration: young are greyish with black spots on the back; mature specimens are pinkish on the sides, grey-blue on the back, with fine blue spots on back and sides, which fade once the fish is dead.
Habitat Lives in inshore waters, most commonly at 15–50m (8–27 fathoms) but occasionally as shallow as 10m (5½ fathoms) and as deep as 200m (109 fathoms). It usually lives over rocky ground, but is found over sandy bottoms in spring and summer.
Breeding In the Mediterranean it spawns in May; it is doubtful whether it breeds in northern European waters at all. It is hermaphrodite.
Food It is an active predator, feeding on fishes, squids and molluscs; its powerful teeth allow it to cope with large prey.
Range Commonly from Biscay southwards to the Canary Islands and throughout the Mediterranean. A rare wanderer in British seas.

Saupe
Sarpa salpa

Family name Sparidae (sea-breams)
Length maximum 45cm (18in); usually about 30cm (12in)

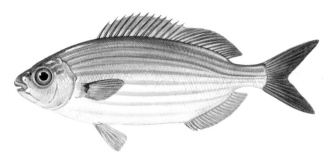

Identification Body oval, smoothly curved above and below; snout bluntly rounded with the mouth slightly on the underside. Eyes relatively small; scales on cheek and gill cover. Teeth in both jaws flattened incisors, and in a single row (moveable on slight pressure); in the upper jaw notched on the cutting edge, in the lower having a single triangular point. A long dorsal fin, the front part spiny (11–12 spines), the posterior part with 14–17 branched rays, its origin above the base of the pelvic fins. Tail fin forked; anal fin low and short, with three spines and 13–15 branched rays. Pectoral fins long. Coloration: greyish-blue with 10–11 thin, golden lengthwise stripes along the sides of the body; lateral line dark; black spot at the base of pectoral fin.
Habitat Lives in shallow water, not deeper than 15m (50ft), usually in only 3m (10ft), near rocks covered with algae or on beds of turtle grass or eel grass. Gregarious, forms tightly packed schools.
Breeding In both spring and autumn. An hermaphrodite, which is a functional male in early life and female later.
Food Adults eat plants and algae; young fish also eat small crustaceans.
Range Throughout the Mediterranean; in the warmer Atlantic from northern Spain to Morocco, Madeira and the Canary Islands. Once recorded from the North Sea.

Saddled Bream
Oblada melanura

Family name Sparidae (sea-breams)
Length maximum 35cm (14in); usually up to 20cm (8in)

Identification Body oval, smoothly rounded in the front, but flattened on the back and belly. Head small, but with large eyes (diameter longer than snout length); scales on cheeks and on the front of the gill covers. Mouth small; each jaw with 8–10 flattened incisors in the front, with a band of smaller teeth behind; in sides of jaws teeth pointed. Dorsal fin long-based with 11 spines and 13–14 branched rays; anal fin shorter and low; pectoral fins long and pointed. Coloration: silvery-grey, back darker; faint darker lines along the sides; a large black spot surrounded by white near the base of the tail fin.
Habitat Forms small schools which swim a few metres below the surface above rocky beds and over turtle grass. Rarely deeper than 30m (98ft). Keeps in more open water than most of the small sea-breams.
Breeding Spawns April–June; some individuals are hermaphrodite.
Food Varied; most feed on small animals but larger fish sometimes browse on algae and scrape the rocks of fine plant fibres.
Range Throughout the Mediterranean; in the Atlantic from northern Spain southwards to Morocco, the Canary Islands and Madeira.

Two-banded Bream

Diplodus vulgaris

Family name Sparidae (sea-breams)
Length maximum 50cm (20in); usually 25–30cm (10–12in)

Identification A rather deep-bodied fish with a pointed snout and slightly concave profile above the eye; eyes moderately large; cheeks and gill covers scaly. Mouth small, lips thick; in both jaws there are eight narrow, light brown, flattened front teeth, with broad, rounded teeth behind them and in the sides of the jaws. Dorsal fin long-based, with 11–12 very strong, sharply pointed spines, the first one above the pectoral fin base, and 13–16 branched rays. Anal fin shorter with three strong spines; tail fin forked; pectoral fin long. Coloration: greyish, occasionally light brown; a black band across the nape extending to the first dorsal spines and the pectoral fin base; a broad black band across the tail extending on to the rear end of dorsal and anal fins.
Habitat Found inshore at 2–70m (1–38 fathoms). It lives over rocky areas and on sandy bottoms; is often found close to algae-covered rocks, and the young in turtle-grass beds.
Breeding Usually spawns October–November, later in the southern Mediterranean, where the larger specimens may breed in early summer. Becomes sexually mature in two years.
Food Juveniles eat algae and small crustaceans; adults are carnivorous, feeding on crustaceans, molluscs and worms.
Range Throughout the Mediterranean; in the Atlantic from the northern Biscay coast to Morocco, Madeira and the Canary Islands.

Annular Bream
Diplodus annularis

Family name Sparidae (sea-breams)
Length maximum 30cm (12in); usually around 20cm (8in)

Identification Body oval, smoothly curved over back and underside. Head relatively small, eyes large; cheeks and gill covers fully scaled. Jaws with eight large, flattened teeth in front and rounded, button-like teeth behind them and in the sides of the jaws, where they are larger. Dorsal fin origin above the base of the pectoral fins, with 11 strong spines and 11–13 branched rays; anal fin with three strong, short spines and 11–12 branched rays. Pectoral fin long and curved. Coloration: silvery-grey on the body, with a dusky spot at the base of the pectoral fin; a broad dark, almost black band around the tail just in front of the fin. Young fish have 5–6 narrow dark bands across the back.
Habitat Shallow water, often in 1m (39in), exceptionally down to 90m (50 fathoms). Young are very common close inshore and in brackish water. This fish lives over sand and eel-grass beds. Abundant in the Mediterranean.
Breeding Spawns late spring–early summer. Matures at about one year, when approximately 10cm (4in) long.
Food Eats worms, crustaceans, molluscs; the young feed on fine algae growing on timber and rocks.
Range Throughout the Mediterranean and the Black Sea. In the Atlantic from northern Biscay to Gibraltar, Madeira and the Canary Islands.

Picarel
Spicara smaris

Family name Centracanthidae (picarels)
Length maximum 20cm (8in) males, 15cm (6in) females

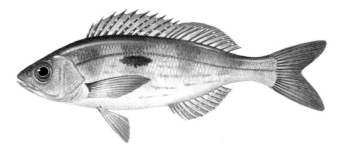

Identification A slender-bodied fish in which the head length is almost equal to the maximum depth of the body. The head is small, and the eye relatively small; the mouth is strongly protrusible, pulling forward into a broad tube. Jaw teeth small and pointed. Dorsal fin long-based, with 11–12 slender spines joined to the 10–12 branched rays. Anal fin shorter but similar shape, with three spines and 8–10 branched rays. Pectoral and pelvic fins small; tail fin forked. Coloration: highly variable with age, sex and season; usually grey-brown above, silvery below; a dusky spot on each side near the end of the pectoral fin. Males have blue-spotted fins when adult.
Habitat Forms huge schools over sandy bottoms in winter at depths of 50–100m (27–55 fathoms). At other times in small groups or even solitary, sometimes at depths as shallow as 15m (8 fathoms). Very abundant in trawl fisheries.
Breeding Spawns in late winter.
Food A generalist feeder on a wide range of bottom-living invertebrate animals.
Range Throughout the Mediterranean and extending into the Atlantic from mid-Portugal down to Morocco.

Damsel Fish

Chromis chromis

Family name Pomacentridae (damsel fishes)
Length up to 15cm (6in); usually around 10cm (4in)

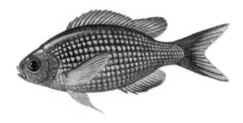

Identification An oval-bodied, rather flattened fish, with a smoothly curved outline above and below. The head is relatively small; the eyes are large; mouth moderate but strongly protractile; teeth small and sharp, in three rows in both jaws. Dorsal fin composed of 13–14 long, sharp spines and 10–11 branched rays; tail fin forked; anal fin with two slender spines and 10–12 branched rays. Head fully scaled; body scales large. Coloration: adults medium brown, the scales outlined in even darker brown; sometimes the centre of the scale is yellowish. Edge of the tail fin pale. Breeding males mauve in colour; young specimens have blue stripes on the body and fins.
Habitat A gregarious fish which forms huge schools in mid-water, usually in close proximity to a reef or a wreck, and sometimes over turtle-grass beds. It is most common at 3–35m (1½–19 fathoms).
Breeding The eggs are laid in summer, usually in a crevice on a rock face within a territory held and defended by the male. Clumps of eggs are stuck by a tuft to rocks and are guarded by the male.
Food All kinds of small planktonic or bottom-living animals.
Range Coastal waters of the Mediterranean and the adjacent Atlantic from mid-Portugal southwards to Angola.

Thin-lipped Grey Mullet

Liza ramada

Family name Mugilidae (grey mullets)
Length maximum about 60cm (24in)
Weight maximum 3kg (7lb)

Identification Streamlined body with a rounded cross-section. Head relatively short but very broad and flattened on top; eyes moderately large, covered with clear tissue, except for very centre. Upper lip is well developed but narrow by comparison with other species; teeth on edge of lip minute and like bristles. Two dorsal fins, the first with four strong, slender spines closely packed at the base but fanning out, second dorsal well separated, with branched rays only. Anal fin similar in shape. Pectoral fins short; if laid forward they do not reach the hind edge of eye. Coloration: grey-blue above, silvery on sides, with several lengthwise grey stripes; white ventrally. A dark spot at the base of the pectoral fin.
Habitat A surface-living fish which forms small schools in inshore waters. It moves northwards during the summer and enters shallow bays, lagoons and even fresh water through river estuaries. It is the most abundant grey mullet in river mouths in salt and fresh water.
Breeding Spawns in the sea in late winter; the young are common in lagoons in the Mediterranean and are cultivated as food fish in enclosures.
Food Algae growing on rocks, timber and larger algae, and small, bottom-living organisms which live in the mud.
Range Whole of the Mediterranean and Black Sea; in the Atlantic from the Baltic southwards to Gibraltar.

Thick-lipped Grey Mullet

Chelon labrosus

Family name Mugilidae (grey mullets)
Length maximum about 75cm (30in)
Weight up to 4.5kg (9lb 15oz)

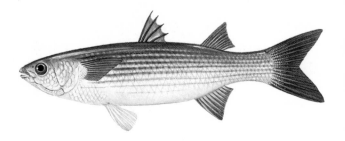

Identification Streamlined body which is rounded in cross-section. Head relatively small; eyes small (diameter less than snout length); lips extremely broad, the lower half of the top lip with coarse, blister-like papillae and closely packed small teeth. Two dorsal fins, the first with four stout spines, close together at the base but fanned out; the second short-based but composed of branched rays. Anal fin similar in shape. Tail fin forked. Pectoral fin pointed; if folded forward it reaches past the centre of the eye. Coloration: dark green or blue-grey above with silvery sides and with 6–7 lengthwise dusky bands. Belly silvery-white.

Habitat Commonly found in coastal waters in small schools mostly close inshore, in harbour mouths, estuaries and in sandy bays. Cruises near the surface, its back breaking the surface in calm weather.

Breeding Breeds late winter–early spring; the young fish make their way inshore and may be caught in intertidal pools in summer.

Food Eats the organic upper surface of mud, filtering out most of the indigestible particles with its gill rakers. Even then, it eats large quantities of fine mud and sand for the small animals therein.

Range From southern Iceland and the northern coasts of Scotland southwards to the Canary Islands and throughout the Mediterranean.

Meagre
Argyrosomus regius

Family name Sciaenidae (drums and shade fishes)
Length maximum 2m (6ft 6in)
Weight up to 65kg (143lb)

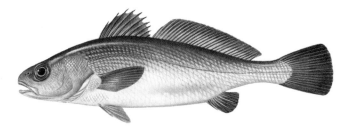

Identification Body elongate, strongly curved on the back, flattened on the belly. Body and head covered with large scales lying obliquely along the body and extending on to the head and tail fin. Head moderately large; mouth big, with numerous small teeth in jaws, a little larger in the outer row; one much larger tooth each side in the lower jaw. Dorsal fins very long-based; the first just separate from the longer second; 9–10 spines in first fin, 26–29 rays in the second. Anal fin very small. Tail bluntly rounded. Coloration: medium brown on the back, silvery sides, with golden reflections on the lateral line scales; inside mouth orange-yellow, fading after death.
Habitat Inshore and shelf waters at 15–200m (9–109 fathoms). Lives mainly close to the sea bed, but migrates in mid-water. Enters estuaries and low-salinity lagoons. A very rare migrant in British seas.
Breeding Usually April–July (southern Mediterranean); not known to breed in northern waters.
Food A wide range of shallow-water and estuarine fishes: grey mullets, sprats, herrings and pilchards.
Range From Norway and Britain (where a rare vagrant) throughout the Mediterranean and along the West African coastline.

Red Mullet
Mullus surmuletus

Family name Mullidae (red mullets or goat fishes)
Length maximum 40cm (16in); usually about 20cm (8in)
Weight maximum 1.6kg (3lb 10oz)

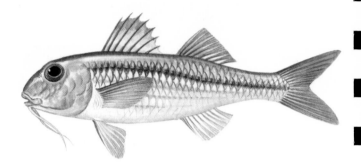

Identification An instantly recognizable fish by its rose-red
coloration and two long barbels on the underside of the chin.
The body is moderately deep and compressed from side to
side; the upper profile of the snout is very steep and the eyes
are set high on the sides of the head. Two rows of scales on
the cheek; scales on head and body very fragile, easily
detached. Two dorsal fins, the first with 2–8 flexible spines,
well separated from the second, which has 7–8 branched rays.
Anal fin similar in shape to the second dorsal. Coloration:
daytime reddish to reddish-brown with 4–5 lengthwise
yellowish stripes and a darker lateral stripe. At night the stripes
break up into a marbled pattern. Alternate yellow and brown
stripes on the first dorsal fin. Colours change soon after death.
Habitat A bottom-living fish, favouring sand or mud, rarely
near rocks, in 3–90m (1½–49 fathoms). It lives in small
schools, probing into the sea bed with its chin barbels for
small food items. Is frequently accompanied by small fish.
Breeding Spawns in summer; the eggs are shed close to the
bottom but float towards the surface. Young fish are at first
silvery-sided surface-dwellers.
Food Bottom-living invertebrates, chiefly worms, crustaceans
and molluscs.
Range From Scottish waters and southern Norway
southwards to the Canary Islands; throughout the
Mediterranean.

Red Band-fish
Cepola rubescens

Family name Cepolidae (red band-fishes)
Length maximum 70cm (28in); usually about half this

Identification Body very long and slender, compressed from
side to side and gradually tapering to a long tail and tail fin.
Head relatively small; eyes large; mouth large with longish
curved teeth in both jaws. Dorsal fin consists of 60770 well-
spaced rays; anal fin nearly as long; pectoral and pelvic fins
small. Coloration: distinctive; back and sides red or orange-
red; belly orange or yellow. Dorsal fin yellowish, but the
anterior part is often dark red. Although much of the colour
fades after death, the body always has a reddish hue.
Habitat Lives in vertical burrows in stiff mud at depths of
17–200m (9–109 fathoms), so is always local in distribution.
Breeding Lays pelagic eggs April–September in the
Mediterranean; details of breeding in northern waters are
poorly known.
Food It lies partly out of its burrow and snatches passing
copepod crustaceans, and probably emerges completely to
feed actively in mid-water.
Range Western coasts of Scotland southwards to Morocco;
throughout the Mediterranean.

Barracuda
Sphyraena sphyraena

Family name Sphyraenidae (barracudas)
Length maximum 1.6m (5ft 3in); up to 60cm (24in)

Identification Body long and slender, rounded in cross-section. Head long and pointed, lower jaw projecting as a sharp point. Mouth large, extending back almost to the level of the eyes, with strong, dagger-like teeth in jaws and roof of mouth. Two dorsal fins, the first with five slender, flexible spines, well separated from the second, which is directly above the anal fin. Tail fin deeply forked; pelvic fin beneath first dorsal fin, well behind pectoral fin. Coloration: dark greenish-brown above, silvery below, with faint dusky bars on body.
Habitat Hovers in mid-water, often close to the surface, waiting for passing fish to approach. Large specimens are often solitary, but young ones form small schools close to the sea bed. Usually 3–13m (1½–16 fathoms) below the surface.
Breeding Spawns May–July in the Mediterranean.
Food Almost entirely smaller fishes, but occasionally eats squids. Large specimens can be aggressive to divers but are now so rare (due to overfishing) that this is not a major problem. All barracudas have to be handled with care.
Range Black Sea and Mediterranean; in the Atlantic from the northern Spanish coast to Morocco and Madeira.

Ballan Wrasse
Labrus bergylta

Family name Labridae (wrasses)
Length maximum 60cm (24in)
Weight maximum 4.25kg (9lb 6oz)

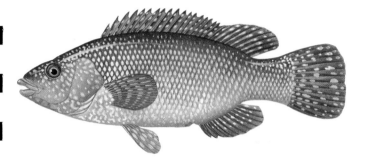

Identification A large wrasse with a relatively heavy, deep body and a moderately large head. The mouth is relatively small, but the lips are fleshy and folded. Teeth in jaws large and strong, in one row; sharply pointed in young fish, worn and rounded in old ones. A long dorsal fin with 18–21 strong spines in the anterior part and 9–13 branched rays in the posterior part. Anal fin shorter, with only three strong spines. Scales large, 41–47 in the lateral line. Coloration: very young fish are pale to dark green, matching the colour of their background; large fish are very variable in colour, usually a reddish-brown, or dark green, and with abundant small white spots overall.
Habitat Lives among algae over rocky grounds and in shore pools and at 2–20m (1–11 fathoms). It is strongly associated with algae, and although it is occasionally caught in open water, this is unusual. Young fish are common in rock pools and in eel-grass beds.
Breeding Builds a nest of fine algae in a crevice in rocks. Eggs are laid in summer.
Food Mainly mussels, plus some crabs and shrimps; their hard shells are crushed by the strong teeth in the jaws and at the back of the throat.
Range From southern Norway and Scottish waters southwards to Gibraltar and Morocco. Absent from the Mediterranean.

Rock Cook
Centrolabrus exoletus

Family name Labridae (wrasses)
Length maximum 15cm (6in); usually around 12cm (4¾in)

Identification A small, deep-bodied wrasse with a short head and small mouth but with thick lips. A single row of small but strong teeth in the jaws. Dorsal fin long, the first section with 18–20 stout spines, joined to the second fin, which has 5–7 branched rays. Anal fin shorter, with 4–6 slender spines and 6–8 branched rays. Scales on most of the head and the body, relatively large, with 33–37 in the lateral line. Coloration: usually greenish or brown, sometimes reddish-brown, lighter on the sides and yellow on the belly. Males have blue spots on the dorsal and anal fins, and on the head. The tail has a dark, crescent mark across it, with a pale band in front and behind.
Habitat Lives in shallow seas, in 2–25m (1–14 fathoms) among algae and eel grass. Mostly found near rocks, but in the eel-grass beds it can be caught over sandy bottoms. It is relatively local in distribution.
Breeding Builds a nest of fine algae in a crevice in rocks and lays eggs May–June.
Food Eats parasites on other fishes, picking them off the skin with its sharp front teeth. Also eats free-living crustaceans such as amphipods and copepods.
Range From northern Scotland and southern Norway southwards to Portugal.

Goldsinny

Ctenolabrus rupestris

Family name Labridae (wrasses)
Length maximum 18cm (7in); usually 12cm (4¾in)

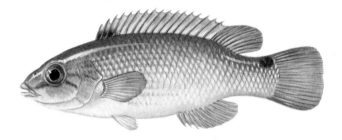

Identification A rather slender-bodied, small wrasse with a small head and moderately large mouth with fleshy lips. Teeth in the jaws in two rows, those in front longer and stronger than at sides. Dorsal fin long, the first section comprising 16–19 slender spines, and continuous with the second section, which has 7–10 branched rays; anal fin shorter but with three slender spines and 6–9 branched rays. Head mostly scaled; body with large scales, 35–39 in the lateral line. Coloration: reddish-brown to orange with a conspicuous black spot on the membrane of the first dorsal fin between the first three or four spines, and another on the back and upper sides near the base of the tail.

Habitat Lives in shallow waters on rocky grounds which are covered with algae at depths of 11–50m (6–27 fathoms), and also over sandy bottoms in dense eel-grass beds in shallower water. Rarely caught in rock pools, on sheltered shores near low-water mark.

Breeding Spawns April–August; eggs believed to be laid in a nest made of plant fibres in a crevice in the rocks.

Food Eats small organisms, particularly crustaceans and worms. Now well known as a parasite-picker for larger fishes.

Range From southern Norway and northern Scotland southwards to Gibraltar and the Moroccan coast; throughout the Mediterranean.

Corkwing Wrasse
Crenilabrus melops

Family name Labridae (wrasses)
Length occasionally reaches 25cm (10in); usually around 15cm (6in)
Weight maximum 320g (11oz)

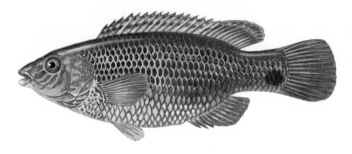

Identification A deep-bodied wrasse, with a moderately large head, a large mouth and small eyes. The lips are very thick; teeth in jaws in a single row, with enlarged teeth in the front. The first bone on the gill cover (preoperculum) is strongly serrated on its rear and lower edges. Dorsal fin long, with 14–17 sharp spines and 8–10 branched rays; anal fin with three sharp spines and 8–10 branched rays. Body scales large, 32–36 in the lateral line. Coloration: very variable, usually green or greeny-brown with darker patches on the back; always a dark spot in front of the tail fin and usually a dark mark behind the eye. Breeding males have reddish marks on the head.
Habitat Abundant over algae-covered rocks from mid-tide level to 30m (16 fathoms). Particularly common in tide pools from mid-shore downwards in sheltered areas where algal growth is abundant. Young ones also inhabit eel-grass beds.
Breeding In early summer builds a nest out of algae in a crevice in rocks, which is guarded by the male. The young are planktonic for a short while but quickly return to the shore and the cover of algae.
Food When young a parasite-cleaner off other fishes. Larger fish eat crustaceans and molluscs.
Range From southern Norway and northern Scotland southwards to Gibraltar and in the western Mediterranean.

Painted Wrasse
Crenilabrus tinca

Family name Labridae (wrasses)
Length maximum 35cm (14); usually 25cm (10in)

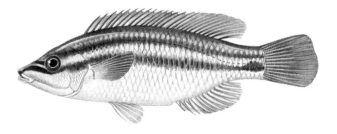

Identification A relatively stout-bodied wrasse, with a large head and small mouth, although the very thick lips make it look much larger than it is. Teeth in jaws strong, with the front teeth much larger than the others. Dorsal fin long-based, with 14–17 slender spines and 9–12 branched rays; anal fin with three spines and 8–12 branched rays. Scales on head small, larger on body, 33–38 in lateral line. Coloration: adult fishes with a dark spot on the side of the body in front of the tail fin, just below the lateral line, and a large black patch on side just above the pectoral fin base. Three or four dusky stripes along the body and fin lengths. Females greenish or pale grey; males greeny-blue with rows of red spots, and top of the head dark blue.
Habitat Lives in inshore waters at 1–50m (3ft–27 fathoms), near rocks and eel-grass beds. Sometimes in saline coastal lagoons. Forms small schools, but breeding males are solitary.
Breeding Male makes nest of plant fibres and guards it. Elaborate display to attract one or more females to lay eggs in it. Breeding takes place April–July. Large specimens are all males, having changed sex.
Food Hard-shelled, bottom-living animals: crabs, shrimps, molluscs and sea urchins.
Range From northern Spain to Gibraltar and throughout the Mediterranean.

Long-snout Wrasse
Symphodus rostratus

Family name Labridae (wrasses)
Length maximum 13cm (5in); usually up to 10cm (4in)

Identification This is a slender-bodied Mediterranean
species, with a pointed, elongate head and snout. Head is
moderate in length but the snout is very long. The lips are
thick; the jaw teeth in a single row are stout. Dorsal fin long,
14–16 slender spines in the front and 9–12 branched rays in
the second part. Anal fin short, with three spines and 9–11
branched rays. Body scales large, 30–35 in lateral line.
Coloration: variable green or brownish with darker marks on
back and sides; usually a pale stripe on top of the head from
lip to first dorsal fin.
Habitat A shallow-water wrasse which can be seen at depths
of 50cm (1½ft) to 20m (11 fathoms), usually among algae,
turtle grass and eel grass. Although it is relatively local, it
occurs in small groups in certain areas.
Breeding The male builds a nest of plant fibres either among
rocks or at the base of eel-grass plants in which one or more
females will lay their eggs. The male guards the eggs, but the
young fish live in plankton for the first weeks of life.
Food Nothing recorded. The snout shape suggests that it has
a specialized form of feeding, possibly in crevices.
Range Throughout the Mediterranean and extending into
the western Black Sea.

Rainbow Wrasse
Coris julis

Family name Labridae (wrasses)
Length maximum 25cm (10in); usually up to 15cm (6in)

Identification A slim, slender-bodied wrasse with a small
head and rather small mouth. Head pointed, snout long and
the jaw teeth (two rows) are sharply pointed. Head without
scales; body with very small scales, 73–80 in lateral line.
Dorsal fin long, with 8–10 slender flexible spines and 11–12
branched rays; anal fin moderately long, with three slender
spines and 11–12 branched rays. Coloration: males have first
three dorsal spines elongate with an orange to deep red spot
on the fin membrane; the back is bluish to olive-green; belly
light-coloured; on sides a zigzag orange to red stripe with a
dark blue to black bar below it on the anterior half. Females
and young have brownish backs with a zigzag brown stripe on
the sides, which becomes reddish in deep water.
Habitat Abundant but solitary and scattered near rocks and
over eel-grass beds in shallow water of 1–30m (3ft–16½
fathoms); old males live deeper, down to 120m (66 fathoms).
Burrows into sand at night or when startled.
Breeding Mostly spawns in summer; the eggs and young fish
are planktonic. Some females change into functional males.
Food Small crustaceans (isopods, amphipods and shrimps),
plus worms and sea urchins.
Range From northern Spain to Morocco and throughout the
Mediterranean. Has occurred in British waters and elsewhere
in northern Europe.

Lesser Weever
Echiichthys vipera

Family name Trachinidae (weevers)
Length maximum 14cm (5½in)
Weight maximum 95g (4oz)

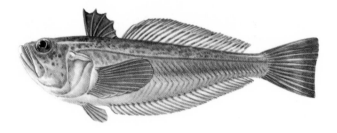

Identification Body rather deep anteriorly but compressed and tapering towards the tail. Head large with a strong spine on the upper gill cover; eyes almost dorsal; mouth large and strongly oblique. The dorsal profile of the head and body almost straight, strongly curved ventrally. Two dorsal fins, the first with 5–6 strong spines, separate from the second, which has 21–24 branched rays; anal fin long, with 24–26 branched rays. Scales absent on cheek, small on body and arranged in oblique, ridged rows. Coloration: yellow-brown on the back, with darker blotches on head and back, ventrally lighter. Membrane to first dorsal fin black.

Habitat Lives in shallow water on clean, sandy bottoms from low-water mark down to 50m (27 fathoms). In tidal areas moves up the beach as the tide advances and back into deeper water as it falls. Burrows in the sand. Is occasionally stood on by bathers and paddlers in this habitat, inflicting a serious and very painful wound.

Breeding Spawns in summer; the eggs are pelagic.

Food Small, bottom-living animals, especially amphipods, small shrimps and young fishes.

Range From northern Scotland and Denmark southwards to Morocco and the Mediterranean.

Note The dorsal fin spines and the gill cover spines have venom glands attached.

Stargazer
Uranoscopus scaber

Family name Uranoscopidae (stargazers)
Length maximum 35cm (14in); usually around 20cm (8in)

Identification Body massive in front, almost circular in cross-section, with top of the head and back flat. Tail compressed from side to side. Head heavy and thickset with hard, rough, bony plates and a massive spine just behind it pointing obliquely upwards. Eyes small, on top of the head. Has a powerful electric organ behind each eye by which it detects approaching prey; lures prey close by wriggling the tentacle on the lower jaw. Mouth strongly oblique with a fringe of small papillae; inside lower jaw a long flap of skin which can be protruded. Two dorsal fins, the first short, with 3–4 spines, separate from the second, with 13–15 flexible rays. Anal fin with one spine and 12–14 rays. Coloration: greyish-brown on back and upper sides, heavily speckled; belly yellowish. First dorsal fin jet black.
Habitat Burrows in soft sand and muddy bottoms at a depth of 15–400m (8–219 fathoms); most common in the upper third of this depth range.
Breeding Spawns April–August; the eggs and young stages are planktonic.
Food Mainly fishes, which are detected by the electric organs and enticed close by the wriggling mouth lure.
Range From northern Spain southwards to Morocco, throughout the Mediterranean and the Black Sea.

Butterfly Blenny
Blennius ocellaris

Family name Blenniidae (blennies)
Length maximum 20cm (8in)

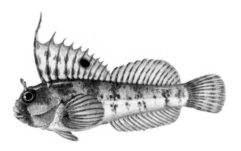

Identification A rather deep-bodied blenny with a
moderately large head, large eyes and small mouth. Teeth in
the jaws small and closely packed. A branched, flattened
tentacle above each eye and small fleshy flaps on the back
beside the dorsal fin. Dorsal fin very high, especially the first
rays, continuous with the soft-rayed second dorsal; anal fin
shorter and lower than second dorsal. Pectoral fin broad; rays
long. Pelvic fins with two long, finger-like rays. Coloration:
greenish-brown or warm brown with several darker bars. First
dorsal fin with a conspicuous black spot ringed with white
midway along it.
Habitat Lives on the sea bed in shallow water of 10–100m
(5½–55 fathoms), but is not found on the shore. It seems to
prefer shell grounds, or sandy and fine gravel bottoms on
which there is a scattering of rocks. It hides in crevices under
stones or beside rocks.
Breeding During spring and summer, the eggs being laid
inside empty mollusc shells or in crevices among rocks and
guarded by the male. The larvae are surface-living at first.
Food Eats small crustaceans, worms and small fishes.
Range Atlantic coast of Ireland, Irish Sea and English
Channel southwards to Gibraltar; throughout the
Mediterranean and western Black Sea.

Tompot Blenny

Parablennius gattorugine

Family name Blenniidae (blennies)
Length maximum 30cm (12in); usually up to 20cm (8in)
Weight maximum about 156gm (5oz)

Identification A thickset blenny with a rather deep body and
a fairly high dorsal fin, with 12–14 quite stout spines and
17–20 branched rays. Anal fin moderately long, with one spine
and 20–21 flexible rays. Pectoral fin broad and fan-like; pelvics
with two longish rays. The head is moderate in size, the eyes
large, each with a large fringed tentacle above it. Mouth small
with thick lips and sharp, closely packed teeth in the jaws.
Coloration: yellowish-brown to medium brown with 7–8
reddish-brown bars across the sides. Eyes also reddish.
Habitat From near low-tide mark down to about 12m (6
fathoms). Small specimens are occasionally found on the low
shore in kelp beds and under other algae. Strongly associated
with rocks and stony sea beds, it lives in crevices and between
stones, emerging to forage in the half light at dawn and dusk.
Breeding Spawns mid-March–April, the eggs being laid in a
crevice guarded by the male.
Food Not studied in detail, but seems to consist mainly of
small crustaceans and worms associated with rocky areas.
Range From northern Scotland and Ireland southwards to
the English Channel and down to Gibraltar; throughout the
Mediterranean.

Red-spotted Blenny

Parablennius sanguinolentus

Family name Blenniidae (blennies)
Length maximum 20cm (8in)

Identification A rather stout-bodied blenny; although the
sides are compressed, the belly sags in a rounded curve. Head
small but deep, eyes high on head; a slender, fringed tentacle
above the eye (about half the eye diameter in length). Dorsal
fin long and of uniform height, with 12 slender spines and 21
soft rays; anal fin shorter, two slender spines and 21 soft rays.
Pectoral fins fan-like but rather small; three long rays in each
pelvic fin. Coloration: olive green to grey-brown with clusters
of reddish spots forming bars on the back and sides, including
the dorsal and tail fins; usually a black spot on the membrane
of the dorsal fin between the first and second rays.
Habitat A shallow-water blenny, most common between
0.5–1m (1½–3ft) but extending down to 5m (16½ft). Hides
between pebbles and in crevices which are exposed to
sunlight; a typical hiding place is at the foot of an algae-
covered rock.
Breeding Lays eggs May–July in crevices or empty mollusc
shells. They are guarded by the male.
Food Eats mostly algae; small animals may sometimes be
eaten by chance.
Range In the Atlantic from northern Spain to Morocco. In
the Mediterranean throughout the western basin, otherwise
mostly along the European coast.

Shanny
Lipophrys pholis

Family name Blenniidae (blennies)
Length maximum 16cm (6¼in)
Weight maximum 85g (3oz)

Identification A slender-bodied blenny with a relatively
large, deep head, noticeably so in large specimens. The only
northern blenny to lack fleshy tentacles on the head. Lips
thick; jaw teeth small, numerous and closely packed, with
relatively massive canine teeth in the angles of the mouth.
Dorsal fin long and low with a notch between the 11–13
slender, spiny rays and the 18–20 soft rays. Pectoral fin
moderately broad; pelvics slender, two rays only in each.
Coloration: usually dark brown or greeny-brown with
indistinct blotching; a darker spot between the first and second
dorsal rays.
Habitat Particularly common on the shore between tide
marks but living as deep as 30m (16 fathoms). Most abundant
on rocky coasts, living in crevices and under algae, but will
also live in shore pools in sandy and muddy situations, where
there are hard surfaces with algae on them.
Breeding Spawns throughout the warmer months of the
year, the eggs being laid in a patch on the underside of a stone
or crevice. They are guarded by the male.
Food All kinds of small animals, notably barnacles,
amphipods and other small crustaceans.
Range From southern Norway and Scotland down to
Morocco, Madeira and the Azores.

Peacock Blenny

Lipophrys pavo

Family name Blenniidae (blennies)
Length maximum 13cm (5in)

Identification A fairly deep-bodied blenny, which is compressed from side to side. Head small, profile of snout steep, almost vertical, lips thick, covering small mouth with slender, closely packed teeth. Dorsal fin long, of even height, with 12 spiny rays and 22 branched rays; anal fin also even, shorter, with two slender spines and 23–24 rays. Pectoral fins broad and paddle-like; pelvics with two rays, both long and flexible. Coloration: basic colour yellowish to green with dark cross-bars, each bar outlined with thin blue stripe; numerous bluish spots on head and lower sides. A black spot, ringed with blue just behind the eye.

Habitat In the intertidal zone and in shallow water down to 5m (2¾ fathoms). Lives mainly in rocky areas but also on sand on which there are isolated boulders. Inhabits crevices of all kinds. Occurs in estuary mouths and low-salinity lagoons.

Breeding Spawns May–July. The males have a high crest of a golden-brown colour and court the females by butting and nodding their heads. Eggs from one or more females laid in a crevice and guarded by male.

Food Mainly bottom-living invertebrates; also algae.

Range From northern Spain to Gibraltar; northern coasts of the Mediterranean.

Montagu's Blenny
Coryphoblennius galerita

Family name Blenniidae (blennies)
Length maximum 8.5cm (3½in)

Identification A small, slender-bodied blenny with a
relatively small head. Profile of head almost vertical; on its
top, stretching between the eyes, is a triangular, fringed flap of
skin, with small tentacles behind it in the mid-line. Two dorsal
fins, united but with a deep notch; first fin with 12–13 slender
spines, the second with 15–18 rather longer rays. Anal fin
shorter, with 17–18 rays. Pectoral fins broad and fan-like;
pelvic fins each with two curved rays. Coloration: greeny-
brown on the back, yellowish on the underside, with dusky
cross-bars running over back and sides. Small, blue-white
spots on the head and back, well developed in adult males
which have an orange edge to the head tentacle and at the
angle of the mouth.

Habitat A shallow-water blenny, occurring in pools on rocky
shores at mid-tide level and below, and in very shallow water.
Most common (but never abundant) on rocks which are
covered with encrusting, coralline algae.

Breeding Lays its eggs in a rock crevice, usually on the roof
of the crevice. The male guards them.

Food Eats mainly barnacles, copepod crustaceans and other
small animals.

Range From the west coast of Ireland, the southern coasts of
the United Kingdom southwards to Gibraltar; throughout the
Mediterranean.

Silvery Clinid
Clinitrachus argenteus

Family name Clinidae (scaled blennies)
Length maximum 10cm (4in)

Identification A slender-bodied fish with a relatively large
head; eyes large, mouth small with fleshy lips. Body covered
with embedded scales which have rough edges. Dorsal fin very
long, origin above head; first section has three slender spines
and is deeply divided by a notch from the second, which has
25–28 slender spines followed by 3–4 branched rays. Anal fin
with two spines and 18–20 branched rays. The pectoral fins
are large and fan-like; pelvics each with two flexible rays.
Coloration: pale green to dark brown with dark cross-bands
across the back and sides, between which there are silvery
blotches.
Habitat Bottom-living in shallow water, but often caught in
depths of less than 1m (39in) down to 4m (13ft). Always in
rocky areas among dense algae and over eel-grass beds in
which it crawls, using its finger-like pelvic fins, propping itself
up on its tail. Swims only when startled.
Breeding Eggs laid May–June. They have short tufts at one end
by which they are attached to algae and rocks. Male guards the
egg-clump, which is often produced by two or more females.
Food Small, bottom-living invertebrates. Diet not well known.
Range Throughout the northern coastline of the
Mediterranean and that of Tunisia and Morocco.

Catfish

Anarhichas lupus

Family name Anarhichidae (sea-cats or wolf-fishes)
Length maximum 1.2m (4ft); usually around 1m (39in)
Weight maximum 11.9kg (26lb 4oz)

Identification Long-bodied, but with a deep, heavy head; the anterior body is also deep but it tapers to a very narrow tail. Head massive but short; eyes very small; mouth large with thick lips; massive teeth in the jaws and in the roof of the mouth. Dorsal fin long, rising above the gill cover and running evenly down to the tail. Minute tail fin. Anal fin about half length of dorsal, uniform in height. Pectoral fin is large and fan-like. Pelvic fins totally absent. Coloration: head and body dark brown, greenish or bluish-grey, with 9–12 darker cross-bars running on upper sides and on to the dorsal fin.
Habitat Lives in deep water of 60–300m (33–164 fathoms), although shallower than this in Arctic regions. Mostly it is caught on hard, rocky bottoms, but sometimes over mud; in the Arctic young fish can be caught in the kelp zone among inshore rocks.
Breeding Spawns in winter; the eggs are deposited as a clump on the sea bed among stones, and among algae in shallow water. The young are briefly found near the surface, but by the age of six months they have become bottom-living.
Food Eats crabs, mussels, whelks, sea urchins and scallops. Its massive teeth crush the shells of these animals with ease.
Range Arctic regions from Iceland southwards to Scotland and Ireland, and the northern North Sea. Also found in the western North Atlantic.

Snake Blenny
Lumpenus lumpretaeformis

Family name Stickaeidae
Length maximum 49cm (19¼in); rarely more than 25cm (10in)

Identification A long-bodied, slender fish, almost eel-like in appearance but with a long tail fin. Dorsal fin long-based, its origin above the pectoral fin base and continuing to the tail fin; fin elements all spiny, those at the front and tail-end short and prickly. Pectoral fin moderately small, rounded; pelvic fins long and slender, flexible. Coloration: pale brown with irregular brownish spots and blotches on the sides and back. Sides with bluish reflections; greenish-yellow on the belly.
Habitat A bottom-living fish on muddy grounds in 30–200m (16–109 fathoms) but most abundant in the shallower end of this range of 40–100m (22–55 fathoms). It is not often captured in trawls but occasionally it has been caught in large numbers. It probably lives in burrows in the muddy bottom.
Breeding Spawns December–January on the sea bed. The larvae are pelagic and occur near the surface February–April.
Food Eats bottom-living invertebrates, small crustaceans, molluscs, brittlestars, sea urchins and worms.
Range From Arctic seas southwards to Denmark and the coasts of England and Ireland. Also occurs off North America.

Butterfish

Pholis gunnellus

Family name Pholididae (butterfishes)
Length maximum 25cm (10in); usually about half this
Weight maximum about 32g (1oz)

Identification A long-bodied fish which is strongly
compressed from side to side. Head short, eyes relatively
small; lips fleshy. The dorsal fin is very long, running from
level with the back of the head to the beginning of the tail fin;
all the fin elements are sharp spines. Anal fin shorter, about
half the length of the dorsal fin, with two short spines and
39–45 soft rays. Pectoral fins small and rounded; pelvic fins
very small, consisting of sharp, thorny spines. Body scales
minute and embedded in the skin; whole fish is incredibly
slimy. Coloration: usually warm brown sometimes greeny-
brown with faint dusky bars on sides. A row of white-ringed
black spots along the base of the dorsal fin.
Habitat In many areas abundant on the seashore between
tidemarks and down to about 100m (55 fathoms). Particularly
abundant on rocky shores and can be found under stones or
among algae.
Breeding Spawns January–February, the eggs being laid in
clumps between stones or inside shells and other cavities, and
guarded either by the female or both parents together.
Food Eats worms, small crustaceans and molluscs.
Range From the White Sea and northern Norway
southwards to the southern coasts of the British Isles. Also
found in North America.

Sandeel
Ammodytes tobianus

Family name Ammodytidae (sandeels)
Length maximum 20cm (8in); usually around 15cm (6in)

Identification Typical sandeel shape, long and thin with a rounded cross-section to the body. The head is pointed, the lower jaw being prominent and sharp; mouth relatively large, extending back to the level of the eyes and protrusible, hinging forwards from the upper lip. Dorsal fin long-based but low, with 50–56 rays; tail fin forked; anal fin about half the length of dorsal fin. Pectoral fins small, placed low down on sides. No pelvic fins. Coloration: clear greeny-yellow on the back, the sides yellow, the belly and lower sides brilliant silver.
Habitat An inshore fish living on clean, sandy bottoms from mid-tide level down to depths of 30m (16 fathoms). Swims in huge schools in mid-water, often at an angle to the surface; if alarmed will dive into the sand and hide.
Breeding Different races spawn in either spring or autumn. Both lay their eggs in the sand, and sand sticks to the surface of them. After hatching, young sandeels are very abundant in the plankton.
Food Eats planktonic crustaceans, fish larvae and the young stages of many invertebrates.
Range From northern Norway and southern Iceland southwards to the Portuguese coast.

Greater Sandeel

Hyperoplus lanceolatus

Family name Amodytidae (sandeels)
Length maximum 30cm (12in)
Weight maximum 225g (8oz)

Identification Long-bodied and slender but circular in cross-section. The head is moderately long and pointed; the lower jaw is prominent and strikingly pointed, but the jaws are not extensible to form a tube. Dorsal fin long, with 52–61 rays, of uniform height; tail fin forked; anal fin low and shorter (about half the length of the dorsal fin). No pelvic fins; pectoral fins small. Scales very small and embedded. A ridge of skin either side of the belly extends back about one-third along the base of the anal fin. Coloration: back and upper sides bluish-green; lower sides and belly brilliant silver. A black smudge on the snout, midway between tip of snout and eye, about the size of the eye.

Habitat An inshore species which is found from just below low-tide mark down to 150m (82 fathoms) on bottoms of coarse sand. It swims in large schools and if alarmed will quickly bury itself in the sand.

Breeding Spawns during spring and summer, the eggs being shed in the sand. The young fish, however, live at the surface.

Food Eats a wide range of crustaceans and fish larvae; as it grows, eats larger organisms.

Range From northern Norway and southern Iceland southwards to northern Spain. Also in the southern Baltic Sea.

Dragonet
Callionymus lyra

Family name Callionymidae (dragonets)
Length maximum 30cm (12in) males, 20cm (8in) females
Weight maximum 155g (5oz)

Identification Head broad and depressed, flat on the
underside, rounded above; relatively large. Body with flattened
belly, but tail rounded in cross-section. Eyes large, sited on
top of the head, close together; mouth moderately large and
strongly extensible. Bone on lower gill cover hooked, with four
strong spines, one facing forwards, three upwards. Dorsal fins
two, both high, the first highest; tail fin long; anal fin short-
based with high rays. Pectoral fin lateral and large, abutting
broad-based, fan-like pelvic fins. Coloration: pale brown with
six brown blotches on the sides and three saddles across the
back. Males have yellow fins with greeny-blue stripes, and blue
stripes and patches on the head and body.
Habitat A locally common fish in water of 20–100m (11–55
fathoms), less commonly down to 200m (109 fathoms). It
partly conceals itself by burrowing in the sand or muddy sand
on which it lives.
Breeding An elaborate courtship display by the male
precedes spawning in spring and summer. The eggs and young
fish are pelagic.
Food A wide range of worms, small crustaceans and
molluscs.
Range From southern Iceland and Norway southwards to
Morocco; throughout the Mediterranean and Black Sea.

Spotted Dragonet

Callionymus maculatus

Family name Callionymidae (dragonets)
Length maximum 14cm (5½in)

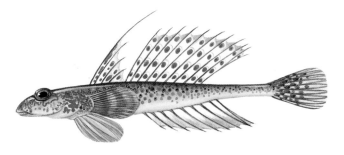

Identification Head and front of body broad and depressed, flattened ventrally; round in cross-section near the tail. Eyes large, sited on top of the head and very close together; mouth moderately large and extensible. Bone on lower gill covers hooked, with four spines, one pointing forward and three upward. Two dorsal fins, both high, particularly in males: the first with four long, spiny rays, the second with 9–10 rays. The tail fin long. Anal fin about same size as second dorsal. Pectoral fins lateral, large; pelvic fins broad-based and fan-like. Coloration: females and young males brownish-yellow on back with two rows of conspicuous brown spots on sides and smaller blue spots. Four brown saddle marks on back. Mature males are similar but the dorsal fins have conspicuous dark spots and pale blue spots.

Habitat Lives on the sea bed, particularly on sandy or muddy grounds, at depths of 70–300m (38–164 fathoms). Seems to be most common on offshore banks.

Breeding Spawns April–June. An elaborate courtship display is presumed. Young fish occur in plankton in summer.

Food No information; presumed to eat bottom-living invertebrates.

Range From southern Iceland and northern Scotland southwards to Morocco and throughout the Mediterranean.

Giant Goby
Gobius cobitis

Family name Gobiidae (gobies)
Length maximum 27cm (11in)

Identification A large, stout-bodied goby with a big head
and deep tail in front of the fin. Scales on nape of head do not
extend to edge of eye. Two dorsal fins, the first with flexible
spines, separated from the longer second fin, which has
branched rays. Anal fin of similar shape but shorter than
second dorsal. Pectoral fins broad and fan-like, with the upper
rays free from the membrane. Pelvic fins fused, forming a disc
with lobes on each side of the front of the membrane. Scales
small, 59–67 between pectoral fin base and tail. Coloration:
brownish-olive or greyish speckled with darker brown and
yellowish dots. Cream underneath. Edges of dorsal and tail
fins pale.
Habitat In northern waters lives on the shore in rock pools,
from the highest pools down to mid-tide level. Elsewhere lives
close to rocks just below low-tide level. Is particularly
associated with bare rocks and green algae.
Breeding Spawns in summer; its eggs are stuck in a patch on
the ceiling of a rock crevice or beneath a rock.
Food Eats large quantities of soft green algae, also
crustaceans, particularly small amphipods and crabs.
Range From the coasts of Cornwall, the Channel Islands
southwards to Gibraltar, and throughout the Mediterranean
and the Black Sea.

Red-mouth Goby

Gobius cruentatus

Family name Gobiidae (gobies)
Length maximum 18cm (7in)

Identification A moderately stout goby with a deep tail immediately in front of the fin. Tail (last dorsal ray to beginning of tail fin rays) about two-thirds of head length. Two dorsal fins, the first separate with six rays, the second with 14 branched rays; anal fin shorter, with 12–13 branched rays. Pelvic fins united to form a disc; front membrane well developed; posterior edge concave. Pectoral fins broad, fan-like, with upper rays divided and separate. Coloration; body warm brown, almost reddish, with darker blotches on sides; lips and cheeks with vivid red markings. Lines of black dots on the head.

Habitat An inshore goby living at depths of 3–4 m (1½–2 fathoms). Most common on rocky grounds with algal cover in sheltered areas in northern seas, but on stones and among eel grass in Mediterranean.

Breeding No data. Probably spawns in spring and summer under crevices, as do most large gobies.

Food No special studies have been made. Probably a general predator on small crustaceans and other invertebrates.

Range In the Atlantic known only from the south-western tip of Ireland, and on the Spanish and Portuguese coasts. In the western basin of the Mediterranean and along the northern coasts of the eastern basin.

Rock Goby

Gobius paganellus

Family name Gobiidae (gobies)
Length maximum 12cm (4¾in)

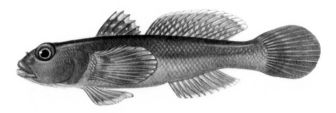

Identification A moderately large, heavy-bodied goby, the tail in front of the fin being deep and its length (end of second dorsal fin to tail fin rays) about half the head length. Two dorsal fins, the first with six unbranched rays, the second with 13–14 branched rays; anal fin shorter, with 11–12 branched rays. Pectoral fin broad and rounded, upper rays finely branched and free from membrane; pelvic fins fused to form a disc; distinct membrane in front with weak lobes either side; many specimens have no lobes. Scales small, 50–57 along sides between head and tail fin. Coloration: dark brown with darker mottling and lighter patches on sides; upper third of first dorsal fin light in colour. Adult males are very dark, and the dorsal fin is orange.

Habitat An inshore goby, abundant in tide pools on rocky coasts or under stones with dense algal cover. Most common from mid-tide level down to at least 15m (8 fathoms).

Breeding Spawns in spring and early summer, the latter further north. The eggs are laid in patches on the underside of rocks or in empty mollusc shells. Sexually mature at 2–3 years.

Food Eats mostly crustaceans (amphipods, isopods and small crabs) and worms.

Range From western Scotland southwards to Morocco, the Canary Islands and Madeira; throughout the Mediterranean.

Black Goby
Gobius niger

Family name Gobiidae (gobies)
Length maximum 17cm (6¾in)
Weight maximum 60g (2oz)

Identification A stout-bodied goby with a large head and big
eyes. Tail deep and short, the length of the tail (last ray of
second dorsal to tail fin) less than two-thirds of head length.
Two dorsal fins, the first branched with six very long rays,
separate from the second, which has 12–13 long branched
rays. Anal fin short-based with 11–12 branched rays. Pectoral
fin broad and rounded, the upper rays divided into fine
filaments. Pelvic fins united to form a disc, the anterior margin
well developed but with no lobes at its edges. Scales large,
35–41 in series along body. Coloration: usually medium to
dark brown, with darker blotches on head, back and sides; fins
dark. Breeding males are particularly dark, with black fins.
Habitat Lives in shallow water, particularly in estuaries and
low-salinity lagoons, at 1–50m (3ft–27 fathoms). It is common
on both mud and sandy bottoms, and over muddy gravel;
occasionally caught in eel-grass beds.
Breeding Lays its eggs in patches under stones or in mollusc
shells; guarded by male. Spawns early spring–August, the
latter further north. Sexually mature at two years of age.
Food Mostly crustaceans (amphipods, isopods, young
shrimps and crabs); also eats worms and small molluscs.
Range From mid-Norway and Scotland, the southern Baltic
Sea (where abundant), southwards to Morocco and
throughout the Mediterranean and Black Sea.

Fries's Goby

Lesuerigobius friesii

Family name Gobiidae (gobies)
Length maximum 11cm (4½in)

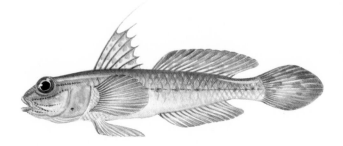

Identification A stout-bodied goby with a rather deep head
and anterior body. Tail relatively slender but shorter than the
head length (tail measured from the last dorsal ray to origin of
the tail fin). Mouth moderate; eyes very large. Two dorsal fins,
the first very high with six flexible spines, the ends of the
spines free of fin membrane. Second dorsal fin distinct, with
13–16 rays. Anal fin a little shorter than second dorsal, with
12–15 rays. Pectoral fins rounded; no rays free of fin
membrane. Pelvic fins form a disc with an anterior membrane
but no lobes at the edges. Body scales large, 28–29 in a lateral
series. Coloration: pale brown or grey with conspicuous
orange or yellow blotches on head, body and fins.
Habitat A bottom-living fish in moderately deep water,
20–350m (11–191 fathoms), on muddy grounds. Makes
burrows in the sea bed, which are also inhabited by the
Norway lobster; the fish acts as lookout near the burrow
entrance.
Breeding Spawns June–August, the eggs being laid in
clusters in the burrow.
Food Mostly worms, but also small crustaceans and molluscs.
Range From southern Norway and the western Scottish
coasts southwards to Gibraltar and along the northern coast of
the Mediterranean.

Transparent Goby
Aphia minuta

Family name Gobiidae (gobies)
Length maximum 5cm (2in) males, 4.6cm (1¾in) females

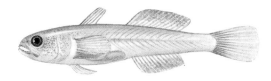

Identification Slender-bodied and compressed from side to side; body transparent, except for pigmented eyes, silvery swim-bladder and gut contents. Head comparatively large, mouth very large. Two dorsal fins, the first with five slender spines, the second with 12 rays; males have longer fin rays than females of same size. Anal fin similar in size and shape to second dorsal fin. Pelvic fins large and well developed in males, much smaller in females; males also have large canine teeth in the jaws. Large scales on body, very easily lost in handling. Coloration: body transparent, a few minute dark speckles on top of head.
Habitat A small, surface-living fish found at depths of about 60m (33 fathoms) in inshore waters, particularly estuaries. Occurs over sand and mud bottoms, and eel-grass beds.
Breeding Spawns May–August. Eggs are laid in empty mollusc shells on the bottom. Sexually mature at one year. All the adults die soon after spawning.
Food Eats small planktonic organisms, particularly copepods, and the larvae of barnacles and other crustaceans, as well as mollusc larvae.
Range From southern Norway and Scotland southwards to Gibraltar; throughout the Mediterranean and Black Sea.

Two-spotted Goby

Gobiusculus flavescens

Family name Gobiidae (gobies)
Length maximum 6cm (2½in)

Identification A slender-bodied goby; although rounded in cross-section at the head and anterior body, the tail is compressed. Eyes lateral, widely spaced, cheeks bulging, mouth relatively small. Two dorsal fins, well separated, the first with seven slender spines, the second with 9–10 branched rays; tail fin rounded; anal fin similar in size to second dorsal, with 9–10 branched rays. Pectoral fins rounded and fan-like without free rays at the upper edge. Pelvics fused into a disc with an anterior membrane. Tail (between last dorsal ray and beginning of tail fin) long and slender, almost as long as the head. Scales large, 35–40 from head to tail fin. Coloration: boldly marked; reddish-brown above with dark reticulations and a series of pale saddles across the back. An intense black spot at the base of the tail fin; males have a second spot behind the pectoral fin.

Habitat An active mid-water goby which lives in small schools close to algae from the surface to depths of 15m (8 fathoms). Quite common in rock pools and among eel grass.

Breeding Spawns May–August. Eggs laid inside the hollow holdfasts of the larger brown algae.

Food Eats small crustaceans, planktonic animals and larvae.

Range From mid-Norway and Scotland, southwards to northern Spain.

Common Goby

Pomatoschistus microps

Family name Gobiidae (gobies)
Length maximum 6.4cm (2½in)

Identification A small, moderately stout goby with a broad
head and rounded anterior body. The tail (from last dorsal ray
to origin of the tail fin) relatively long, nearly as long as the
head, and narrow. Two dorsal fins, the first with six flexible
spines well separated from the second, which has 8–9
branched rays. Anal fin similar in shape to second dorsal, with
8–9 branched rays. Pectoral fins rounded, broad, with no free
rays. Pelvic fins united to form a disc; anterior membrane with
indentations on edge. Coloration: grey to fawn, with 4–5 pale
saddles across the back and a dark reticulation on the back
and sides. A diffuse black spot at the beginning of the tail fin, a
less distinct spot on the upper base of the pectoral fin; in males
a conspicuous black spot at the end of the dorsal fin, and
dusky bars on sides.
Habitat Inshore and inter-tidally in brackish pools and
estuaries, salt marshes and tidal pools near high-tide mark. In
winter migrates into deeper water.
Breeding Lays eggs April–August in a hollow mollusc shell
or under crevices in small stones. Breeds several times each
year. Few live more than 18 months.
Food Small crustaceans, particularly amphipods, copepods
and mysids, worms and even insect larvae.

Painted Goby
Pomatoschistus pictus

Family name Gobiidae (gobies)
Length maximum 9.5cm (3¾in); usually around 6cm (2½in)

Identification A small, rather stout-bodied goby with a
moderately narrow head; tail long and narrow, its length (last
dorsal ray to beginning of tail fin) nearly as long as head. Two
well-separated dorsal fins, the first with six slender spines, the
second with nine branched rays; anal fin similar in shape, with
8–9 branched rays. Pectoral fins rounded; pelvic fins fused to
form a disc. Body scales large, 34–43 in lateral series, no scales
on head or nape. Coloration: warm brown or fawn with a
network of darker dots on the scale edges; five conspicuous
white saddle marks across the back and tail, and five double
diffuse dark spots on the sides of the fish. Dorsal fins with a
conspicuous line of dark spots on lower membrane; in males
an orange edge to the fin.
Habitat Lives inshore from low-tide mark to 50m (27
fathoms) on gravel and stony bottoms, shell and coraline
algae. Also lives on sand close to eel grass and algae. Young
specimens can be caught occasionally between tide-marks on
stony bottoms.
Breeding Spawns April–July; the eggs are laid in empty
mollusc shells and guarded by the male.
Food Small crustaceans, amphipods, copepods and worms.
Range From mid-Norway and northern Scotland southwards
to northern Spain.

Sand Goby

Pomatoschistus minutus

Family name Gobiidae (gobies)
Length maximum about 9.5cm (3¾in); usually about
6cm (2½in)

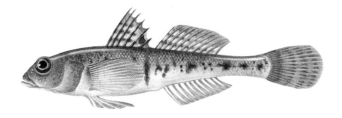

Identification A very abundant small goby, rather slender in
body shape and with a long, narrow tail (last dorsal ray to tail
fin, nearly as long as the head). Two well-separated dorsal
fins, the first with six slender spines, the second with 10–12
branched rays; anal fin similar in length to second dorsal but
lower, with 9–12 rays. Pectoral fins rounded; no free, finely
divided rays on the upper edge. Pelvic fins fused to form a
disc, the edge of the anterior membrane with small, finger-like
processes. Body scales small, 58–70 between the pectoral fin
base and the tail; scales present on the nape and the breast.
Coloration: light sandy brown with a fine network of dark
dots. Males with four dark bars on back and sides; females
with 4–5 dusky spots along sides.
Habitat Inshore sandy grounds from about mid-tide level to
20m (11 fathoms). Most common just below tide level.
Abundant in estuaries but not in low salinities. Moves into
deeper water in winter.
Breeding Spawns February–July; the eggs are attached to the
roof of a small cavity, often a mollusc shell or a hollow pebble.
Food Eats small worms and crustaceans.
Range From northern Norway to southern Spain, including
the Baltic Sea. Common on all British coasts.

Mackerel
Scomber scombrus

Family name Scombridae (mackerels and tunnies)
Length maximum 66cm (26in); usually around 40cm (16in)
Weight maximum 2.8kg (6lb 2oz)

Identification Relatively slender-bodied but rounded in cross-section; the head and body streamlined. Two dorsal fins, well separated from each other and followed by a series of five finlets; 11–13 slender spines in first dorsal. Anal fin relatively small, also followed by five finlets. Tail fin widely spread and forked with two keels on its base; pelvic fins small, lying in shallow depression; pectoral fins relatively small. Coloration: brilliant blue-green on the back with black curved lines sometimes forming spots. Sides white with pinkish and gold reflections. The brighter colours fade quickly after death.
Habitat A fish which forms huge schools near the surface and in mid-water from the coast out to the edge of the continental shelf. Strongly migratory, they move northwards, as well as inshore, in summer, and the opposite direction in winter. Now heavily overfished, so less common than formerly.
Breeding Spawns May–August; eggs and larvae float near the surface.
Food Young fish eat plankton, particularly crustaceans, fish and other larvae. Adults feed heavily on small fishes, such as sandeels, sprats and young herring.
Range Atlantic Ocean, from northern Norway to Morocco and on the North American coast. Throughout the Mediterranean and in the Black Sea.

Blue-fin Tunny
Thunnus thynnus

Family name Scombridae (mackerels and tunnies)
Length maximum 4m (13ft); not often over 2.6m (8ft 6in)
Weight maximumt 385kg (850lb)

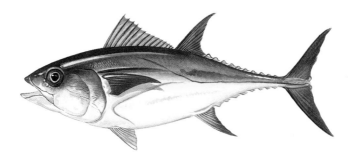

Identification A stout-bodied, streamlined fish; spindle-shaped body, round in cross-section. Two dorsal fins, the first with 13–15 slender spines, high in front and concave in outline; this fin can be depressed into a slot, so as not to be obvious. Second dorsal short with high rays, followed by finlets. Similar finlets following the anal fin. Tail fin narrow and widely spread. Small keel at the base of each tail fin lobe; a larger one on the sides of the body. Pectoral fin moderately large, about twice the length of pelvic fin. Scales all over the body, those on the front larger than elsewhere. Coloration: back dark blue, shading to green on sides; belly white. The finlets are greyish-yellow.
Habitat A migratory fish living in the surface layers of the ocean down to about 100m (55 fathoms). It rarely comes close inshore, and then only where the shore is adjacent to deep water. Moves northwards during summer.
Breeding In the Mediterranean in summer; the eggs and larvae are surface-living. May live up to 30 years.
Food Young eat crustaceans and small fishes; adults eat fishes and squids, particularly fishes which form large schools.
Range From Norway south to southern Africa and along the North and South American coasts. Throughout the Mediterranean. Now much scarcer than formerly owing to overfishing.

Bonito
Sarda sarda

Family name Scombridae (mackerels and tunnies)
Length maximum 1m (39in); usually around 60cm (24in)

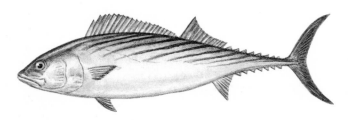

Identification Elegant, streamlined shape; the head is pointed and rather long, the upper jawbone extends beyond the eye. Two dorsal fins; the first dorsal, with about 20 spines, longer in front, and tapering in height until it almost touches the second dorsal fin; a series of 8–9 finlets behind both the second dorsal and the anal fins. Tail with a distinct keel; two small keels at the base of the tail fin lobes. Coloration: steel blue to dull green on back, with 10–12 oblique black lines running upward; sides silvery-yellow.
Habitat An open-ocean fish living in small schools, frequently leaping from the water as it pursues prey. Strongly migratory in north European seas and moving northwards in summer; common off southern Europe. Mostly offshore, and from surface to 50m (27 fathoms).
Breeding Spawns in early spring in the warmer parts of its range. The eggs and young fish are pelagic.
Food Eats mostly fishes, including pilchards, sprats, herring, flying fishes and scad. Also eats large quantities of squids.
Range From Scotland southwards, mostly on open-ocean coasts. Throughout the Mediterranean and the Black Sea. Southwards to southern Africa and across both the South and North Atlantic.

Swordfish
Xiphias gladius

Family name Xiphiidae (swordfishes)
Length maximum 4.9m (16ft); average around 2m (6ft 6in)
Weight maximum 450kg (1000lb)

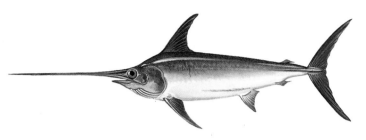

Identification Unmistakable on account of its long bill and heavy, thickset body anteriorly. The body tapers towards the tail and the tail fin is narrow but with enormously high lobes. A single keel either side of the body just in front of the fin. In adults two dorsal fins, the first high and short and the second a small finlet. The anal fin is also divided into two, the second part being small. In young fish these fins are part of a single dorsal and a single anal fin, the middle rays being lost during development. The pectoral fins are rather long and curved; no pelvic fins. Coloration: grey-blue above, paler beneath; belly almost white.

Habitat An open-ocean fish which ranges through the upper layers of the sea from the surface to 610m (334 fathoms). The adults seem to be solitary or at most form loosely organized schools. Strongly migratory, they enter cool northern seas in the summer.

Breeding Spawns in spring and summer in large schools. The eggs and young are pelagic.

Food Large numbers of squids and schooling fishes such as pilchards, mackerel, small tunnies and herring-like fishes.

Range Worldwide in temperate and tropical seas. In Europe from mid-Norway southwards, but rare in the north.

Frigate Mackerel
Auxis rochei

Family name Scombridae (mackerels and tunnies)
Length maximum 60cm (24in); usually around 35cm (14in)

Identification Moderately slender-bodied, but still bullet-shaped and round in cross-section, typical of the family. Two well-separated dorsal fins; the first is high in front, the upper edge strongly concave; the second is small and followed by eight small finlets. Anal fin small, also with a series of finlets behind it. Tail fin narrow, lobes widely spaced. A keel on the sides of the tail, and smaller keels above and below it at the base of the fin lobes. Pectoral fins short. Large scales on anterior body, running down the lateral line in a wide band. Coloration: blue-green or dark blue on the back, silvery on sides and belly. It has a series of about 15 dark, wavy bars along the back.
Habitat A pelagic schooling fish in open seas in tropical and warm temperate regions, which moves northwards and inshore with the warm season. Schools congregate near inlands on ocean coasts.
Breeding Spawns November–August in subtropical areas.
Food Eats small schooling fishes, particularly pilchards, and other herring relatives; also eats squids and crustaceans, especially in their pelagic life-stages.
Range Uncommon wanderer in British seas, travelling as far north as Denmark. From Biscay southwards, and common in the Mediterranean. Widespread in all warm seas.

Brill
Scophthalmus rhombus

Family name Scophthalmidae (left-eyed flatfishes)
Length maximum 75cm (30in); usually about 50cm (19½in)
Weight maximum 7.2kg (16lb)

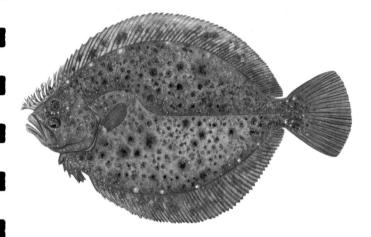

Identification A broad-bodied, heavy-headed flatfish with eyes on the left side of the head (i.e. if laid with white side down, the mouth and eyes face the left). Dorsal fin origin close to tip of snout, the first rays free of the fin membrane. Pelvic fins broad-based, first rays on coloured side in advance of those on the blind side. Body covered with small scales on the coloured side, embedded in the skin on the white side. Coloration: warm sandy brown with small dark flecks and lighter spots; fins lighter, with less obvious spots.
Habitat Lives on the sea bed on sandy bottoms, but may be common on gravel banks and mud. Adults live at 9–73m (5–40 fathoms). Young fish live very close to shore, even in sandy shore pools; they move into deeper water as they grow.
Breeding Spawns in spring and summer; the eggs and larvae are pelagic. Bottom-living when 20–35 mm (¾–1¼in) length, moving inshore as they develop.
Food A wide range of bottom-living fishes, especially sandeels and whiting, small squids and large numbers of crustaceans.
Range From southern Norway and Scotland southwards to the Mediterranean and the Black Sea.

Turbot
Scophthalmus maximus

Family name Scophthalmidae (left-eyed flatfishes)
Length up to 1m (39in); usually 50–80cm (20–32in)
Weight maximum 15kg (33lb)

Identification Body very broad, head large with huge mouth; both eyes on left side of head (i.e. when fish laid white side down, belly towards the observer, the eyes are on the left). Dorsal fin long, origin in front of upper eye, the rays branched but only their extreme tips are free of fin membrane. Pelvic fins long-based, equal in size. Dorsal fin rays 57–71; anal rays 43–52. Body scaleless but with scattered bony tubercles embedded in skin on head and body, sometimes only on blind side. Black Sea specimens heavily covered with tubercles. Coloration: warm sandy brown with darker spots and speckles covering the back and fins. Cream-coloured ventrally.
Habitat Inshore waters from just below the shoreline to about 80m (44 fathoms) on gravel, shell-gravel and sandy bottoms. The colour of the eyed side is an exact match for the sea bed on which it lives. Young fish live close inshore, often between tide-marks on sandy shores.
Breeding Spawns during spring and summer. Eggs and larvae are pelagic and drift inshore, becoming bottom-living when 2.5cm (1in) at up to six months old.
Food Gobies, sandeels, pouting and smaller flatfishes.
Range From southern Norway and Scotland southwards to Gibraltar; throughout the Mediterranean and Black Sea.

Megrim

Lepidorhombus whiffiagonis

Family name Scophthalmidae (left-eyed flatfishes)
Length maximum 60cm (24in); usually about 35cm (14in)
Weight maximum 1.7kg (3lb 12oz)

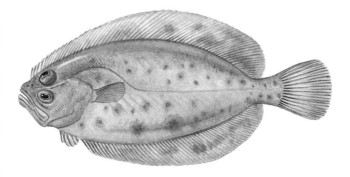

Identification A rather narrow-bodied, compressed flatfish
with a moderately large head, a big mouth and huge eyes. The
eyes are on the left side of the fish (i.e. if laid white side down,
belly towards the observer, the eyes are on the left). Dorsal fin
long-based, origin about the level of the nostrils; the ends of
the first 10 rays free from the margin. Both dorsal and anal
fins curve under the tail and their last rays are on the
underside. Dorsal rays 85–94; anal rays 64–74. Pelvic fins
broad-based, their bases equal in length. Coloration: back pale
yellow-brown with dusky patches; pure white on underside.
Habitat A deep-water flatfish, living on muddy bottoms at
depths of 50–300m (27–164 fathoms). It may also be caught
on sand.
Breeding Spawns in spring in deep water; eggs and larvae
planktonic. The young fish take to bottom-living at a length of
19mm (¾in) when both eyes are present on the left side of the
head.
Food Eats mainly bottom-living fishes, including gobies,
dragonets, sandeels and small members of the cod family, as
well as flatfishes and crustaceans.
Range Offshore from southern Iceland, Scotland and
Norway to Gibraltar and the western Mediterranean.

Eckström's Topknot

Phrynorhombus regius

Family name Scophthalmidae (left-eyed flatfishes)
Length maximum 20cm (8in)

Identification A moderately wide-bodied flatfish with a rather short head, large, strongly oblique mouth and large eyes which are almost touching. The outline of the snout is deeply notched in front of the upper eye. Both eyes on left side of head (i.e. when the fish is laid white-side down, belly towards the observer, the eyes are on the left). Dorsal fin begins in front of the upper eye and ends as a distinct lobe on the underside of the tail; anal fin also ends under the tail. Pelvic fins long-based, equal in size, not joined to anal fin. Body covered with small scales, toothed on eyed side, giving the coloured surface a rough texture; on blind side scales smaller and less rough. Coloration: warm brown with irregular dusky patches; a more distinct blotch on the middle of the side.
Habitat A sparsely distributed but widespread fish living on rough grounds with rocks and sand. May cling to underside of rocks and be hard to catch rather than rare. Lives at depths of 9–55m (5–30 fathoms).
Breeding Spawns April–June; its eggs and young are pelagic.
Food No data available.
Range From west coast of Scotland south to Gibraltar and in the western Mediterranean.

Topknot

Zeugopterus punctatus

Family name Scophthalmidae (left-eyed flatfishes)
Length maximum 25cm (10in)
Weight maximum 350gm (12oz)

Identification A wide-bodied, almost rectangular-shaped,
flatfish with a large head. The mouth is large and nearly
vertical, and the eyes are moderate in size but not touching.
Dorsal fin very long-based, its origin on the tip of the snout
and its end forming a distinct lobe on the underside of the tail;
anal fin also forming distinct lobe. Pelvic fins long-based,
equal in size and joined to the anal fin by a distinct membrane.
Scales, with fine teeth on the upper side, give body a rough
feeling. Eyes on left side of head. Coloration: warm brown on
the eyed side, with irregular dusky mottling; rounded dark
blotch on the middle of coloured side; bold, dark, curved lines
running through eyes and across to sides.
Habitat Lives in shallow water of 1–25m (3ft–14 fathoms),
but also caught on the shore in rock pools. Particularly
adapted to life on rocky grounds, where it clings to the
underside of rocks and other hard structures, the whole
underside forming an adhesive disc.
Breeding Spawns offshore in spring; eggs and larvae pelagic.
Food Not well known. Possibly small fishes and crustaceans.
Range From southern Norway, Shetland and Scotland south
to southern Biscay; confined to rocky areas.

Scaldfish

Arnoglossus laterna

Family name Bothidae (scaldfishes)
Length maximum 19cm (7½in)

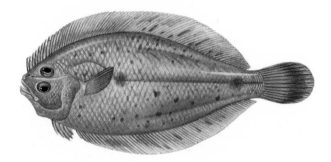

Identification A small flatfish with a relatively narrow, almost oval body; head rather small, eyes large, mouth moderate and oblique. Both eyes are on the left of the head (i.e. if fish laid white-side down, belly to the observer, the eyes will be on the left). Dorsal fin begins in front of upper eye; the first 10–12 rays partly free of fin membrane but not elongate. Pelvic fin on eyed side long-based, much larger than fin on blind side. Dorsal fin rays 87–93; anal rays 65–74; scales thin and fragile, usually missing from body. Coloration: pale brownish-grey with darker spots on body and fins; pelvic fin with a dusky spot.

Habitat A common fish in inshore waters of 10–60m (5½ to 33 fathoms), occasionally caught at 5m (2¾ fathoms). It is most common on sandy grounds but also occurs on mud. Its abundance in such areas as the North Sea means that it must be important in the ecology of bottom-living animals.

Breeding Spawns in spring and summer; the eggs and larvae are pelagic. Larval development may continue for several months; the young fish are about 3cm (1¼in) when they become bottom-living.

Food Not studied. Probably eats small crustaceans.

Range From southern Norway and Scotland southwards to Gibraltar and throughout the Mediterranean. Very common in the North Sea and Irish Sea.

Plaice

Pleuronectes platessa

Family name Pleuronectidae (right-eyed flatfishes)
Length maximum 1m (39in); usually around 50cm (20in)
Weight maximum 4.6kg (10lb 3oz)

Identification Body deep and compressed, with a small head. Both eyes on the right side of the head (i.e. if the fish is laid white-side down, belly towards the observer, the eyes are on the right). Jaws relatively small, the teeth on the lower jaw stronger than those on eyed side. Dorsal fin rising above upper eye, running to tail; anal fin shorter, with 48–59 rays. Lateral line straight; body scales small and smooth, mostly embedded in the skin. A line of 4–7 bony knobs beginning between the eyes and extending to gill cover. Coloration: back warm brown with bold red to orange spots; blind side clear, pearly white.
Habitat A bottom-living fish with a wide range of habitats from sand or shell-gravel to mud, in depths of a few inches to 200m (109 fathoms). It is most abundant in 10–50m (5½–27 fathoms). Large fish come into the tidal zone to feed and the young ones are often found in shore pools on sandy beaches.
Breeding Spawns January–March, usually in depths of 20–40m (11–22 fathoms). The eggs are pelagic, as are the young fish for up to six weeks, after which they settle on the sea bed at a length of about 18mm (¾in).
Food Mainly molluscs, crustaceans and worms.
Range From northern Norway and Iceland, southwards to Gibraltar and the western Mediterranean. Especially common in the North Sea, the Irish Sea and the English Channel.

Flounder
Pleuronectes flesus

Family name Pleuronectidae (right-eyed flatfishes)
Length maximum 50cm (20in)
Weight maximum 2.6kg (5lb 11oz)

Identification A close relative of the plaice. Its body is
relatively deep and compressed, with a small head. Eyes on
the right side of the head (i.e. if laid white-side down and belly
towards the observer, the eyes will be on the right). 'Reversed'
specimens (eyes on the left side) may be encountered. Dorsal
fin, origin above upper eye, continues to tail; anal fin shorter,
with 35–46 rays. Both fins have sharp prickles at the bases of
the rays. Lateral line straight, also with a patch of prickles at
its end over the pectoral fin; body scales smooth, partly
embedded. Coloration: dull brown, even greenish-brown, with
indistinct dark patches; sometimes with pale orange spots.
Blind side dull white, sometimes with pale brown blotches.
Habitat A common flatfish on sandy or muddy bottoms,
from the tide-line to about 55m (30 fathoms). Also found in
estuaries and fresh water, particularly in the north of its range.
Breeding Spawns at 25–40m (14–22 fathoms) over sandy
bottoms. The eggs and young are surface-living, but the young
drift inshore and at about 3cm (1¼in) long migrate into rivers.
Food Bottom-living invertebrates such as cockles, worms and
shrimps; young fish eat bottom-living freshwater invertebrates.
Range From the White Sea, northern Norway south to
Morocco, the Mediterranean and the Black Sea; particularly
common in the Baltic, the North and Irish seas.

Dab
Limanda limanda

Family name Pleuronectidae (right-eyed flatfishes)
Length maximum 42cm (17in); usually up to 25cm (10in)
Weight maximum 1.25kg (2lb 12oz)

Identification A moderately small flatfish, with a rather deep body and small head. The mouth is small but the eyes are relatively large. Eyes on the right (i.e. if fish laid white-side down, the belly towards the observer, the eyes are on the right). Dorsal fin, origin above the upper eye, continues to tail; anal fin shorter, with 50–64 rays. The lateral line is strongly curved above the pectoral fin; the body scales are small, heavily toothed on the eyed side so that the surface is rough to the touch. On the blind side only the scales along the edges of the body are toothed and feel rough. Coloration: warm sandy brown with small, darker freckles on the eyed side; white on the blind side.
Habitat An abundant flatfish in shallow water of 20–40m (11–22 fathoms), with some found at only 2m (1 fathom). Young fish are common in shallow water. Most abundant over sandy bottoms, but also occurs on shell-gravel and mud.
Breeding Spawns offshore in spring and early summer. The eggs and young fish are pelagic, but at a length of 13–18mm (½–¾in) the young move inshore and are bottom-living.
Food Eats most bottom-living invertebrates, particularly crustaceans, polychaete worms and molluscs.
Range Occurs from the White Sea and northern Norway, Iceland and Scotland southwards to southern Biscay. Very abundant on the continental shelf of the British Isles.

Lemon Sole
Microstomus kitt

Family name Pleuronectidae (right-eyed flatfishes)
Length maximum about 66cm (26in)
Weight maximum 1.1kg (2lb 7oz)

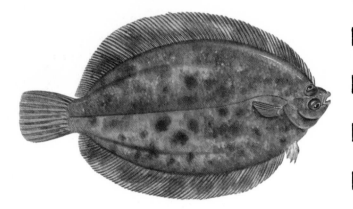

Identification Body a smooth oval with a small head and protuberant mouth (shape similar to a lengthwise section of a lemon), plus the tail fin. Eyes on right side of the head. Dorsal fin long, rising above the upper eye and almost reaching the tail fin; anal fin shorter, also reaching the tail fin. Body scales smooth-edged, embedded; skin very smooth to touch. Shallow curve in lateral line above the pectoral fin. Coloration: warm brown with irregular dark brown markings and flecks of yellow and green on eyed side; white on blind side.
Habitat Widely distributed in northern Europe and common locally. Lives mainly on sand and gravel bottoms in depths of 40–200m (22–109 fathoms), particularly in offshore areas of shallow water. Less often found on muddy grounds. Small specimens can be caught very close inshore.
Breeding Spawns in spring and summer in depths of about 100m (55 fathoms). Eggs and young fish float near the surface; post-larvae live in mid-water and from a length of 3cm (1¼in) they live on the sea bed.
Food Eats mostly polychaete worms, but also crustaceans and some molluscs.
Range From the White Sea and northern Norway, Iceland and Scotland southwards to southern Biscay. Particularly common in the northern North Sea.

Halibut
Hippoglossus hippoglossus

Family name Pleuronectidae (right-eyed flatfishes)
Length maximum 2.5m (8ft 3in); rarely above 2m (6ft 6in)
Weight maximum 106kg (234lb)

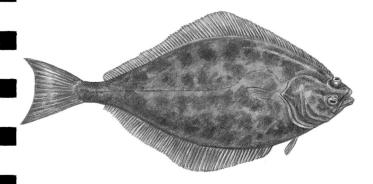

Identification A massive flatfish, which is slender-bodied
and thickset. The head is large, as is the mouth; lower jaw is
prominent; both jaws have moderate-sized teeth. Eyes both on
the right side of the head. Dorsal fin origin is level with the
front edge of the upper eye, continuing on to the tail. Anal fin
shorter. Tail fin slightly concave or square-cut. Scales on body
small, embedded in skin; a strong curve in the lateral line over
the pectoral fin. Coloration: dull greeny-brown, sometimes
almost white; the blind side is pearly white.
Habitat A deep-water flatfish which is found at 100–1500m
(55–820 fathoms), although the younger ones may be found at
depths as shallow as 30m (16 fathoms). Lives on a wide range
of bottoms – sand and gravel and even rocky grounds – but
frequently hunts in mid-water.
Breeding Spawns in winter and early spring close to the sea
bed in deep water. The eggs drift in mid-water, and the young
start living on the bottom at around 3.5cm (1½in). Young fish
live nearer the shore than adults.
Food Adults eat a wide range of deep-water fishes, often
quite large ones; young halibut feed mostly on crustaceans.
Range Arctic seas from Spitzbergen southwards to western
Ireland, and on the North American coast.

Sole
Solea solea

Family name Soleidae (soles)
Length maximum about 60cm (24in); usually up to 40cm (16in)
Weight maximum 3kg (6lb 10oz)

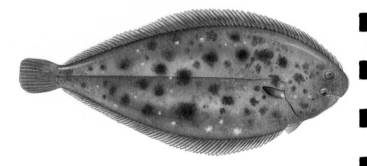

Identification Slender-bodied and oval, with the eyes on the right side of the head, i.e. if laid white-side down with the vent nearest to the observer, the eyes are on the right. Head small, eyes small and protruding above the surface but the exposed side covered with skin; mouth ventral and curved. Dorsal fin origin in front of upper eye. Dorsal and anal fins joined to the tail fin base by a membrane. Pectoral fins small; that on the blind side only a little smaller than the other. Nostril on the blind side swollen; short 'whiskers' over the underside of the head. Scales with teeth; feels very rough to touch. Coloration: medium to dark brown on the eyed side, with darker patches; pectoral fin with a black spot. Blind side creamy white.
Habitat A common bottom-living fish at 10–100m (5–55 fathoms), although young fish can be caught in intertidal pools and among breakers. Most common on sandy bottoms, but does live on mud bottoms. Usually buries in the sand in daylight, but swims into mid-water at night and may migrate by swimming at the surface.
Breeding Spawns in spring and early summer in shallow water. Eggs and early young are pelagic; young fish bottom-living at 13mm (½in).
Food Eats mostly small crustaceans and worms.
Range From Scotland and Norway south to Morocco and in the Mediterranean. Abundant in the North and Irish seas and the English Channel.

Solenette
Buglossidium luteum

Family name Soleidae (soles)
Length maximum 13cm (5in)

Identification Typically sole-like in body form, with elongate, flattened body, rounded head and snout, and tapering tail. Head small, gill opening restricted; eyes small, their upper parts covered with skin, their diameter much less than snout length; mouth strongly curved. Dorsal fin origin in front of upper eye, low and extending to the tail fin; anal fin shorter, also low; pelvic fins broad-based. Pectoral fin on eyed side small, that on blind side vestigial, reduced to one long ray and two small ones. Coloration: sandy or yellowish-brown freckled with brown spots; every fifth or sixth ray of dorsal and anal fins black almost to the tip.

Habitat A small offshore sole common on sandy bottoms in depths of 5–40m (3–22 fathoms), although occasionally found deeper than that. Its biology has not been fully studied but it probably burrows in the surface of the sand by day and is active by night.

Breeding Spawns during summer; the eggs and larvae are pelagic. From a length of about 13mm (½in) the young fish lives on the bottom.

Food Eats small crustaceans and worms.

Range From southern Norway, Denmark and Scotland, south to western Africa; throughout the Mediterranean.

Thick-back Sole
Microchirus variegatus

Family name Soleidae (soles)
Length maximum 33cm (13in)

Identification Body shape typical of the soles, elongate with a slender body, but in this case thick from side to side, with a smoothly curved snout. The head is small, mouth curved, strongly on the underside; eyes rather large, their diameter greater than the snout length. Dorsal fin origin almost in front of upper eye, fin smoothly curved in outline; anal fin shorter. Pectoral fins small, that on the blind side minute. Nostril on the blind side tubular, not expanded into a rosette. Coloration: chestnut brown on the back with five darker cross-bands creating dark patches on dorsal and anal fins. White ventrally.
Habitat A sole living offshore in depths of 37–92m (20–50 fathoms) but occasionally both shallower and deeper than that. It is most common on sand or sand and gravel bottoms. Its biology is little known and in northern Europe it is a relatively uncommon fish.
Breeding Spawns in deep water in spring and early summer. The eggs and young fish are pelagic at first, but the post-larvae gradually seek deeper water, and from 18mm (¾in) they live on the sea bed.
Food Bottom-living invertebrates; no detailed studies are available.
Range From western Scotland (where rare) southwards to western Africa and the Mediterranean.

Trigger-fish
Balistes capriscus

Family name Balistidae (trigger-fishes)
Length maximum 40cm (16in)
Weight maximum 2.4kg (5lb 5oz)

Identification Deep-bodied but with compressed sides. The head is large with moderate-sized eyes and a very restricted gill opening each side just above and in front of the pectoral fin. Mouth with large, chisel-like rat teeth in jaws. Dorsal fin in two sections, the first with three strong, roughened spines, the first of which cannot be depressed unless the second spine is depressed. Second dorsal fin long-based, high in front, similar in size and shape to anal fin. Tail fin with long outer rays. Pelvic fin reduced to a coarse, roughened spine. Body covered with hard, bony plates. Coloration: olive brown or greyish; the fins with faint blue lines.

Habitat Lives in mid-water, often close to rocks and pier pilings in 5–30m (2¾–16½ fathoms). Since about 1980 has become fairly common on the southern and western coasts of Britain (previously only one or two were reported each year). Often caught by anglers and in crab and lobster pots.

Breeding Nothing reported in European waters. Elsewhere eggs are laid in a cavity excavated by the female and guarded by the male.

Food Crustaceans and molluscs such as mussels.

Range From the west coast of Scotland southwards to West Africa, throughout the Mediterranean. Also on the North American Atlantic coast.

Puffer-fish
Lagocephalus lagocephalus

Family name Tetraodontidae (puffer-fishes)
Length maximum 60cm (24in)

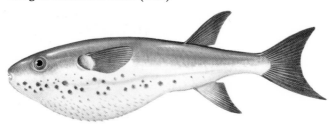

Identification Quite unmistakable. Long-bodied but circular in cross-section, with the belly capable of inflation; the skin normally rather loose. Coarse prickles on underside of head and body. Dorsal fin short-based but high with curved outline; anal fin similar in shape, slightly posterior. Tail fin concave. The head is rather large and smooth-skinned, with small, lateral eyes; gill opening small and restricted, just in front of pectoral fin. Four strong teeth in the jaws, forming a parrot-like beak. Lateral line a raised fold of skin along the side and crossing over the back. Coloration: bright blue to steel blue on back; belly pure white; small dusky spots on sides.
Habitat A surface-living fish of the open ocean, widely distributed in all tropical seas and occurring rarely as a vagrant in northern European waters in late summer. Very little is known about its biology.
Breeding No data available.
Food Eats squids and crustaceans living in the surface waters of the ocean.
Range From western Scotland, where a rare vagrant, more common in the western English Channel and southwards. Throughout the Mediterranean. Elsewhere in all tropical seas.

Sunfish
Mola mola

Family name Molidae (sunfishes)
Length maximum 4m (13ft);
usually around 2m (6ft 6in)
Weight maximum
450kg (1000lb)

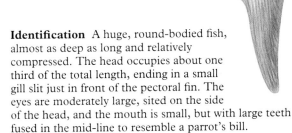

Identification A huge, round-bodied fish,
almost as deep as long and relatively
compressed. The head occupies about one
third of the total length, ending in a small
gill slit just in front of the pectoral fin. The
eyes are moderately large, sited on the side
of the head, and the mouth is small, but with large teeth
fused in the mid-line to resemble a parrot's bill.
The dorsal and anal fins are short-based but very high; they
are approximately the same size. The tail fin is a thick fringe
with a wavy edge at the rear of the body. Coloration: generally
greyish-brown or dark blue, darker above, paler below.
Habitat An open-ocean fish which occurs at depths of
183–366m (100–200 fathoms), but is occasionally found
floating side-up at the surface, even in inshore waters. These
surface-floating fishes are probably disabled.
Breeding Eggs very small and numerous. Place and season of
spawning not known. The young fish go through a series of
developmental stages when they are covered with spines.
Food Large quantities of jellyfishes, salps and comb-jellies;
also eats crustaceans at the ocean surface.
Range Worldwide in tropical and subtropical seas, drifting
northwards into European waters due to oceanic circulation.
Throughout the Mediterranean.

Index

RSNC

The Royal Society for Nature Conservation is pleased to endorse these
excellent, fully illustrated pocket guide books which provide invaluable
information on the wildlife of Britain and Europe. Royalties from each
book sold will go to help the RSNC's network of 48 Wildlife Trusts
and over 50 Urban Wildlife Groups, all working to protect rare and
endangered wildlife and threatened habitats. The RSNC and the
Wildlife Trusts have a combined membership of 184,000 and look
after over 1800 nature reserves. If you would like to find out more,
please contact RSNC, The Green, Whitham Park, Lincoln LN5 7NR.
Telephone 0522 752326.